C000155535

EMMERDALE'S YORKSHIRE

James Ferguson

WEIDENFELD AND NICOLSON
LONDON
By arrangement with Yorkshire Television Limited

Text Copyright © James Ferguson, 1990.
Photographs courtesy of Yorkshire Television
Stills Department © Yorkshire Television
Ltd, 1990. Emmerdale is a Registered Trademark of
Yorkshire Television Ltd.

Series created by Kevin Laffan

Executive Producer Keith Richardson
Producer Stuart Doughty
Story Editor Morag Bain
Script Editor Ann Tobin

Published in Great Britain by
George Weidenfeld & Nicolson Limited
91 Clapham High Street
London SW4 7TA

All rights reserved. No part of this publication may
be reproduced, stored in a retrieval system, or transmitted,
in any form or by any means, electronic, mechanical,
photocopying, recording or otherwise, without the prior
permission of the copyright owner.

ISBN 0 297 81122 3

Frontispiece: Esholt Village

Printed in Great Britain by
Butler & Tanner Ltd,
Frome and London

Contents

Introduction

Every week, more than 11 million viewers share the lives of the characters who live at Emmerdale Farm and Beckindale. In this way, Annie Sugden, Seth Armstrong and the others are almost as well known as members of our own families.

Each of us feels we know them so well because we watch them at work and at home, but in fact we seldom share their quieter moments. We see them on screen because they have generously allowed us to become involved with moments from their busy lives.

But how do these popular Yorkshire people spend their own leisure time? Where do they go and what do they do when they are not on such public view?

Eight of the characters have allowed us to accompany them as they visit favourite areas within their own county. We join Annie, Joe, Henry Wilks, Dolly, Seth, Alan Turner, Kathy and Rachel as each shows us a little of their own special part of Yorkshire.

Annie's peaceful abbeys

HAD anyone suggested to Annie Sugden that a June visit to Fountains Abbey in the Yorkshire Dales would have prompted her to modernise her famous kitchen, she might have regarded them with that renowned 'no-nonsense' glare. Jack had often said that a glance from his mother could stop a charging bullock at twenty paces, but it was indeed while exploring that majestic ruin that the notion came to her.

Early one Wednesday morning, after Jackie's tragic death, she had wanted to be alone with her thoughts and memories. At such times of family sadness, she appreciates the tranquillity and calming sense of peace within the hallowed walls of abbeys and churches. Although she does not resent the presence of others, knowing that their reason for visiting might be similar to hers, she does try to arrive earlier than the general public. Some do recognise her, however, and so, throughout the year, she quietly shares her peaceful moments with strangers and well-wishers. Annie knows that she is never totally alone, and in that knowledge there is comfort.

But when the ruined abbeys and churches become very busy, Annie will discreetly leave to go about her daily work, knowing that when the need for solitude arises, there are many wonderful places of peace within easy reach of Beckindale.

The beautiful abbeys and churches of Yorkshire provide one of her deepest pleasures. There she can reflect upon her life with its sadnesses as well as its times of great happiness; she can feel pride in the new generation which now forms her expanding family and she can privately express the sorrow that her dear father, Sam Pearson, no longer shares her life and her joys.

From time to time, therefore, she will leave her busy kitchen at Emmerdale, sometimes telling Joe, Kate or one of the others that she is going shopping at Harrogate, York or Skipton, but in fact she will divert from her route to call at an abbey or church. On occasions, she spends an entire day visiting a selection; some are well known and consequently busy with tourists, such as York Minster, Beverley Minster and Ripon Cathedral, while others are almost as impressive but lack the charisma of the tourist centres – in the latter case, she includes the Cathedrals of Bradford and Wakefield, or St Peter's Parish

Church in Leeds. This is the only parish church in England which retains daily sung services in the cathedral tradition.

In addition, there are gems in quiet places and some contain real treasures – the tiny Kirkdale Minster, near Kirkbymoorside, for example, is concealed in a deep valley where it was built around AD 654. It is the oldest complete church in Yorkshire, being some five centuries older than either Fountains Abbey or Rievaulx Abbey.

And it is still in use. Above the door is a Saxon sundial, the most complete example of its kind in the world and it bears the longest known inscription from Anglo-Saxon times. Not far away is the parish church of Lastingham whose origins are as ancient as Kirkdale Minster. Beneath it is an apsidal crypt which is a complete church in its own right. It is one of very few in the country and the only one complete with chancel, nave and two side aisles. This crypt is more than 900 years old and is probably built over the grave of St Cedd, thus being his shrine. It is even more remarkable because it has not been altered since 1088 – or to make the date more significant, since William the Conqueror was in England. When descending into this crypt from within Lastingham church, Annie is aware of the links between its tiny size and the massive splendour of Fountains Abbey.

It was the Conqueror who gave Stephen, the abbot of Whitby Abbey, permission to move to Lastingham to establish an abbey and a community. But Stephen did not finish that work. Instead, he moved on to York to found what became St Mary's Abbey and it was the monks of St Mary's who, a few years later, left York to establish Fountains Abbey. But in leaving Lastingham, Stephen left this astonishing crypt, his own unfinished abbey.

Annie Sugden.

Throughout the county, there are other churches with Saxon remains, such as Leathley, Hovingham, Skipwith and the tiny minster at Stonegrave in Ryedale. Dating from the eighth century, Stonegrave Minster continues to serve as a parish church. It is one of Yorkshire's four minsters, the others being York, Beverley and Kirkdale. The term 'minster' has not been applied to any church built since the Reformation, for it signifies a church which belonged to a monastery as opposed to a cathedral which is the chief church within a bishop's diocese. A minster can, however, also be a cathedral – like York.

It is not unusual for the remains of a past monastery or abbey to serve as a modern parish church – there are several in Yorkshire. One is the remarkable eleventh-century Selby Abbey which became a parish church in the reign of James I. One of England's most noble cathedrals, it has avoided mass tourism, but high on the list of visitor attractions is the elegant Bridlington Priory on the Yorkshire coast. This also serves as a parish church. Dating from 1113, it was one of the wealthiest of Augustinian houses, only its splendid nave and gatehouse surviving Henry VIII's onslaught at the Reformation. From time to time Annie spends a few moments here in quiet prayer; she remembers with affection the times she used to visit Matt and Dolly when they spent their summer holidays at Bridlington with young Sam.

It was during such a holiday that Annie discovered the King and Queen of Holderness – they are two magnificent churches. The King is the cathedral-like church at Hedon while the Queen is the elegant church at Patrington. Each seems too large and imposing for these East Yorkshire villages.

Beverley Minster, near the edge of the Yorkshire Wolds, is noted for its Frid Stool. This rare possession, a simple stone chair over 1,000 years old, was endowed with the right of sanctuary. After King Athelstan, the first King of All England, gave his Charter of Freedom to the church at Beverley, fugitives would take refuge here by sitting on this stool.

11

ABOVE LEFT *Ampleforth Abbey is a modern community of Benedictine monks and adjoins Ampleforth College, Britain's leading Roman Catholic public school for boys.*

ABOVE RIGHT *Byland Abbey, once the largest Cistercian church in England, has the country's largest nave. The abbey lies in a peaceful valley near Coxwold in North Yorkshire although the original plan was to construct it at Old Byland on the hills above. But the bells of nearby Rievaulx were intrusive and disturbed the monks at prayer, so they moved their church to this serene location.*

But in a county which has more abbeys than any other in England nothing surprises Annie. She knows that Yorkshire contains some of the country's finest examples of ecclesiastical architecture, both past and present; consequently her choice is wide-ranging. She has made a determined effort to include Rievaulx, Jervaulx, Easby, Kirkham, Monk Bretton, the stunning Mount Grace Priory near Ingleby Arncliffe and Newburgh Priory at Coxwold, which is used as a private house but which contains the body of Oliver Cromwell in a vault in the roof. From time to time, when she shops in Leeds, she spends an hour or two in the city's Kirkstall Abbey which is one of the nation's best preserved ruins and which, according to an obelisk nearby, is exactly midway between London and Edinburgh, being precisely 200 miles from each.

By complete contrast, there is the living abbey of Ampleforth with its modern community of Benedictine monks, or the deserted stones of Whitby where the British method of determining the date of Easter was established in AD 664. For sheer size, little can compare with Byland, the largest Cistercian church in England.

But when pressed to nominate her favourite abbey, Annie will always say Fountains Abbey. Unsurpassed throughout Britain for sheer splendour and beauty, it is astonishingly complete in its remote North Yorkshire dale. She can always make time for one of her private, early visits, never tiring of its setting and constantly discovering some new aspect of its history. Recently she has re-discovered the panorama presented from Surprise View and she has speculated as to whether Robin Hood really did draw water from the well that bears his name.

But it was one Wednesday morning in June when, with some humour and surprise, she discovered so many Emmerdale features about the abbey! For one thing, Fountains Abbey was a successful farming enterprise, and at the height of its influence and prosperity it was a leading livestock centre with thousands of sheep on the surrounding fells. Having been awarded the title of Defender of the Faith by the Pope, King Henry VIII then decided to leave the Catholic church and he dissolved all its monasteries while establishing his Church of England. At the time, Fountains Abbey possessed 2,356 horned cattle, 1,326 sheep, 86 horses, 79 pigs, 117 quarters of wheat, 12 quarters of rye, 90 quarters of malt and barley and 2 quarters of oats. In charge at the time was the thirty-eighth and last abbot whose name was Marmaduke Bradley.

It was his painful duty on 26 November 1539 to surrender Fountains Abbey and its belongings to the commissioners of Henry VIII. Construction of the abbey had begun four centuries earlier, around 1132 by a band of twelve monks from York. They were Benedictines who sought a more disciplined life as Cistercians, so with their prior they had trekked to the wilderness of Skeldale. It was a fertile, wooded valley four miles from Ripon but was severely overgrown. An old account said, 'It had never been inhabited unless by wild beasts, being overgrown with wood and brambles, lying between two steep hills and rocks, covered with wood on all sides. It was more a retreat for wild beasts than humans.'

There was no shelter other than the trees and nothing to eat, but the monks had an unshakeable faith in God. The land had been given to them by Archbishop Thurstan of York and it was rich with mineral springs and natural fountains. As a consequence, they dedicated their proposed building to Our Lady of the Springs – Sancta Maria de Fontibus. The name of Fountains is said to come from *fontana,* the Latin for spring or fountain. Furthermore, the

When Annie Sugden goes shopping in Leeds, she will sometimes visit the city's Kirkstall Abbey, one of the nation's best preserved ruins. It stands close to the River Aire and is exactly half way between London and Edinburgh; it is also very close to Yorkshire Television's Leeds studios.

name of the River Skell which flows through the valley is also said to mean fountain, although some believe the name honours the founder of the Cistercian order of monks, St Bernard. He was born at Fontaines in Burgundy. Whatever the source of its name, this beautiful building is known throughout the world as a splendid tribute to ancient workmanship and an undying faith.

In extremely primitive conditions, and eating the leaves of trees to survive, the monks began their task, sometimes sheltering beneath a massive elm or making use of some yew trees for cover. Even now, after so many visits, Annie finds it difficult to comprehend that such a stunning church had such an unpromising start. But by the sixteenth century, long after the death of its founders, Fountains Abbey had grown beyond all their dreams and had rapidly prospered through its highly successful wool trading. Another abbey which was also successful at wool trading and sheep farming was Rievaulx which lies near Helmsley.

Between them, these were probably the two most successful wool trading centres in the north of England, with an immense overseas trade, especially to Venice and Florence. Indeed, the origin of Yorkshire's famous woollen and textile industry owes much to Fountains Abbey, with modern industrial skill stemming directly from those medieval monks. Indeed, the Emmerdale flock of Mashams is part of that tradition, albeit on a small scale.

At its prime as a sheep farm and wool producer, Fountains Abbey was of great value to Henry VIII in his acquisition of wealth, but this beautiful creation was spared the wanton destruction of so many other abbeys. Most of the internal fittings and furniture, along with some glass, woodwork and various roofs, were removed, but the building itself suffered little structural damage. For that reason, much of its original stonework has survived.

In exploring these extensive ruins, Annie Sugden found more comparisons with her own modest abode. Fountains and Emmerdale owned some of Yorkshire's broad acres – even if the 60,000 or so belonging to Fountains did expand into several Yorkshire dales, including Nidderdale, Upper Wharfedale, Ribblesdale and Malhamdale, in addition to pastures, corn fields, lead mines, quarries, fisheries and game preserves! It was said that a monk of Fountains might walk in a straight line for thirty miles without leaving the monastery's lands. It made Emmerdale's 300 acres look puny by comparison, even if the external buildings were so similar.

But like Emmerdale, Fountains Abbey had once been surrounded by buildings which housed its cattle and sheep, with immense storage space and huge arable areas under cultivation, just like a large, modern farming enterprise.

Annie had marvelled at the astonishing *cellarium*, two long parallel and adjoining corridors stretching for over 100 yards and supported by graceful and slender columns over an earthen floor. It was so like a church within a church that it was difficult to imagine it had been merely a massive storeroom for huge numbers of woolpacks. Now she realised why the Woolpack Inn in Beckindale was so named – it is yet another reminder of links between this abbey and the woollen industry of the dales.

Whitby Abbey on its magnificent cliff-top site. It was here in AD 664 *that the British method of calculating the date of Easter was established. The abbey is also the birthplace of English poetry through Caedmon. Once a cowherd at the abbey, he found himself able to sing in verse of the Creation, the origins of mankind and many other religious topics. The abbey stands on top of the town's famous 199 steps.*

Annie had often tried to visualise the enormous activity at Fountains during its peak. As its vast flock of moorland sheep roamed the Yorkshire fells, the monks and their helpers would have had all the problems of the modern sheep farmer, such as diseases and thieves. They'd have known the hard work and heavy losses at lambing time as well as incidentals like the maintenance of dry stone walls and clearance of ditches.

At the abbey there would be non-stop activity with traders coming and going as business deals were struck. A dairy herd was maintained, too, but one abbot had the sense to employ milkmaids who were anything but beautiful – being a wise man, he felt that lovely young milkmaids might be too much of a temptation for the younger monks or their helpers, the lay brothers!

Horses, carts and wagons would gather as the people went about their trading, and at times the abbey's exterior would look like a thriving market place, probably rivalling that of nearby Ripon, York or Skipton. The abbey served as a bank, too, and corn was milled here, so far from being a place of peace and solitude it must have been a continuing bustle of activity. The vehicles which had assembled at that time probably equalled in number those which arrived nowadays at the car park during peak visiting times! As Annie strolled between the venerable stones, she tried to draw comparisons between the sheepshearing and lambing times of Fountains and Emmerdale, but decided that Fountains would have coped much more easily because they had many more helpers!

Another more mundane similarity was the parlour. Just as Emmerdale Farm has a parlour, so does Fountains Abbey and its remains can be seen. The name 'parlour' comes from the French *parler* which means 'to speak' and it was here that the monks were allowed to talk to one another. Because so many rooms and other places within the massive building demanded the observance of silence, the abbey had set aside this room for brief conversation, but any chatter had always to be short and to the point, with no gossiping.

Another place of interest was the cloister area because it was here that the monks lived and relaxed while not at work in the church or the fields.

Annie began by examining the dining area known as the refectory, the washing area (*lavatorium*) with its semi-circular trough, the sanitary area (*dormitorii necessaria*) with its primitive but effective flush toilets which made use of local streams. Even now, some Yorkshire folk refer to outside toilets as nessies! There was the warming house, too, (*calefactorium*) where a log fire, for the benefit of all the monks, burned from All Saints Day (1 November) until Easter. She wondered if they were sometimes allowed to talk in here? 'I bet they did,' she smiled to herself on one occasion.

But it was the kitchen, known as the *coquina,* which interested Annie Sugden most. She learned that the word 'cook' comes from *coquere,* hence the Latin name for the abbey's kitchen.

Even in its present state she could visualise the primitive conditions of the original room. Divided into two rooms by a pair of massive fireplaces standing back-to-back, it had a door leading to the cloister and another to the refectory, with high windows looking over the cloister roof. Above was a wooden floor, access to which was by ladders and this was a storage space for the more immediate kitchen requirements. The kitchen was one of the few places (apart from the warming room) that had a fire in winter, which made it very popular with the monks. During the cold weather they would find excuses to visit the kitchen, just as Joe and the others always manage to find excuses to visit Annie's kitchen at Emmerdale when the kettle is on!

The monks of Rievaulx Abbey, near Helmsley, were major producers of wool, and their other interests included fishing and agriculture. St Aelred, one of its abbots, said the abbey provided a marvellous freedom from the tumult of the world.

The astonishing cellarium at Fountains Abbey. Two long parallel and adjoining corridors stretch for over 100 yards and are supported by graceful and slender columns over an earthern floor. Although this looks like a church, it was a massive store-room and contained huge numbers of woolpacks.

To avoid overcrowding and to allow the vital work to continue without interruption, the abbot instructed that only the cooks for the week, the abbot's cook and the monk in charge of the infirmary were allowed into the kitchen! However, at times when there was no fire in the warming house, the precentor could enter the kitchen to soften the wax of the tablet he used to enter the names of those who were to officiate at Mass or take a special part in the coming week's services. The drying of parchment was also allowed in the kitchen and a monk was allowed to bring that in; the sacristan was permitted to enter too, but only to obtain a light for the candles or incense, or to get a little salt for purifying the holy water.

Annie thought the monks' food sounded very plain. Although it was better than the diet of leaves which had supported the first monks, it was far from nourishing and not as appetising as a Yorkshire farmhouse meal. The brethren rose very early without eating and their breakfast consisted of a little bread and wine about 9 am. Dinner (or lunch as it is called in some areas) followed at noon and comprised a pound of bread and two dishes of vegetables served separately. These were cooked without fat. Supper was between 6 pm and 7 pm and consisted of the remains of the bread used at dinner with perhaps some raw fruit or vegetables. The meals were eaten in silence except for one monk who read from the gospel while his colleagues ate.

One of the abbots refused to allow extracts from the Old Testament to be read aloud because he felt it was too saucy and exciting for the celibate brothers! To ensure silence at meals, there was a requirement that 'nuts must not be cracked with the teeth, but opened silently with a knife.' During the winter months, dinner was at 3 pm with no supper to follow, although a drink of water was allowed.

It was while reflecting upon this tough way of life and studying the primitive kitchen that Annie decided she must update her own kitchen. As she pondered upon the basic facilities at Fountains Abbey, she realised that, at its prime, this kitchen would have been a superb example of the very latest and up-to-date, a splendid example of what a kitchen should be.

So what about her old kitchen? Quite suddenly she decided it was terribly out of date! And so, with no more ado, she decided to rip out her old kitchen and replace it with something modern and bright. When she returned to Emmerdale that day, having gone straight from Fountains Abbey into Harrogate to examine some kitchen styles and units, she set about her task. The result can now been seen by visitors to Emmerdale. But she did like the way the abbot kept people out of his kitchen when the cooks were busy, and she is thinking of introducing some of his rules!

Bolton Priory provides Annie with a further source of fulfilment and happiness for it lies within a few minutes drive of Emmerdale. Beautifully established in a delightful rural setting in gentle Wharfedale, this former Augustinian priory attracts visitors by the thousand, just as it has attracted artists like Turner and Landseer, poets like Wordsworth and writers like the Brontës. As with Fountains, Annie manages to arrange her visits so that they occur during those quiet lulls between the Priory's busier times. In comparison with many, Bolton Priory lacks structural splendour even if its location is a dream, although like Bridlington Priory the nave survives to form a parish church. The neighbouring village bears the conflicting name of Bolton Abbey, but the building is a priory, i.e. a monastery governed by a prior instead of an abbot.

It stands very close to the Harrogate–Skipton road (A59) and attracts a host of visitors but the area seldom seems overcrowded because there are such delightful walks beside the River Wharfe. Visitors seem to filter into the all-embracing countryside, crossing the river by a stout wooden bridge as they explore the woodlands or climb the hills towards the awesomely named Valley of Desolation. A large area around Bolton Priory has been declared an area of special scientific interest by the Nature Conservancy Council because it is host to some unusual plants and many species of birds.

Flowers and plants must not be picked, and dogs should be kept on leads. There is a mystery too – from time to time, even in daylight, the ghostly figure of a monk has been sighted among the ruins!

But a walk along the river banks beyond the priory has its special rewards. A short distance from the ruin, the river narrows to create the infamous Strid. This is where the banks close in until the river roars through a narrow channel

Fountains Abbey is Britain's most spectacular ruined abbey and is unsurpassed for beauty and splendour. Beside the gentle River Skell, some four miles from Ripon, it became a prime sheep-farming community and wool producer whose enterprise and skills led to the creation of the modern textile industry of West Yorkshire.

19

Bolton Priory stands close to the A59 Harrogate–Skipton road and attracts thousands of visitors each year. The ruins of this former Augustinian priory contain a twelfth-century church which is still in use.

which tempts the unwary to attempt a leap across – on one occasion, Annie had to prevent the impulsive young Jack from attempting this leap. It is here, so guide books tell us, that many young men have lost their footing on wet and slippery rocks, and have perished in the waters below because the gap is wider and more dangerous than it appears.

No one knows how many lives have been lost here, but the most famous was William, the son of Lady Adeliza (or Alice) de Romille. His untimely death lives on in the legend of the Boy of Egremont. Born at Egremont Castle in Cumberland, he was staying at Bolton with his mother. His elder brother had died and so he was heir to the family's vast estates. According to the legend, he was enjoying a hunting expedition in the woods beside the Wharfe when he came upon the Strid. With his greyhound on a leash, he thought he could easily jump across and attempted to do so while clutching the leash. But at the final moment the dog hung back and dragged its master backwards. Both fell into the roaring chasm and were drowned.

Lady Adeliza was so distraught that she gave the land to the Augustinian canons so they might build a church to his memory. The legend has been re-told by many writers, including William Wordsworth who interpreted the legend in his poem 'The Force of Prayer'. One interesting aspect is that the land was handed over to the monks by the ceremonial laying of a knife on the high altar of the local church. Annie Sugden had re-told this legend to her own tiny children as a warning of the dangers of the Strid. She had often taken them on picnics to Bolton Priory where they enjoyed the freedom of running around the ruins and among the trees. Now, she had fond memories of those times with young Jack, Joe and Peggy, although Peggy, too, had later died in a tragic accident.

She knew the legend would be passed down through her own family, but from time to time did wonder if her own story telling had nurtured Jack's love of literature.

Now in her maturing years, Annie Sugden continues to be a regular visitor to Bolton Priory, often going for a long walk by the Wharfe in the very early morning as the birds are singing and the countryside is fresh with dew. But when asked which was her favourite place of prayer and peace, she replied, 'I'm surprised that you ask me that! It's our own parish church, of course! St Mary's in Beckindale!'

This occupies one of the oldest sites in Beckindale and has been a centre of worship for centuries. The Saxons built a wooden church and the Normans rebuilt it in stone, parts of which can still be seen in the north door. The font is Norman but the tiny church underwent large-scale structural alterations in the sixteenth century, one reminder of which is the pulpit, carved by Italian craftsmen. However, the rood screen is later and probably dates from the seventeenth century. Subsequent renovations obliterated much of the church's earlier history, but it still remains the focal point for worship in Beckindale.

As Annie said, 'It has seen Sugden family births, marriages and deaths, and if you could see our little church in the autumn, with its pews full of contented Beckindale folk and every shelf and ledge filled with the ripened fruits of the harvest from our farms and the dales around us, then you'd know why it means so much.'

At the point known as The Strid, the River Wharfe roars through a narrow channel which tempts the unwary to leap across. Many have tried and failed. One victim was William de Romille, known in legend as the Boy of Egremont Castle. He was dragged into the Wharfe by his dog while attempting this leap. Upon his death, his mother asked that Bolton Priory be built in his memory.

2

Joe goes racing

THROUGHOUT his life, Joe Sugden has been interested in horses but has always been too busy to devote to them as much time as he would have wished. If he had been wealthier, he would have purchased a string of racehorses and some hunters; if his plans for the development of NY Estates had succeeded, he would have had the space and the accommodation (and hopefully the money!) to fulfil that earnest desire. But Joe is a realist. He knows that ownership of horses costs a great deal of money and time, far more than he can currently afford. Emmerdale Farm and his new family must take priority.

But, as he often tells himself, if he works hard and diligently, he could still own at least one racehorse and perhaps a fine hunter or two. That is one of his aims.

But he can and does assuage his continuing interest by riding across the fells and along the lanes. He also enjoys a day's racing at one of Yorkshire's splendid courses. Sometimes he meets Alan Turner there, more by chance than by agreement, and sometimes he meets old friends from his young days as a competitive rider. Joe has ridden at most of the Yorkshire courses, both on the flat and over the jumps. He has even scored a few wins, something he will mention when pressed by Kate, or when Rachel and Mark ask about his youthful days.

Another of his happy memories was when he introduced Jackie Merrick to racing. Poor Jackie has been taken from his family by a tragic shooting accident but during that first day's racing at York, Joe had explained the intricacies of betting, the meaning of the differing odds, the tote system and the whole panoply of horse racing. Jackie had thoroughly enjoyed himself. Even so, he had not found the racing game as absorbing as Joe did, in spite of winning a few pounds – and losing a few more!

When Joe had worked for NY Estates, he had made an effort to visit the Thirsk regional office when there were race meetings at Thirsk's small and pleasant course. This remains one of his favourites, although he is the first to admit that each of the nine Yorkshire courses has its own charms, style and characteristics. Glamorous York, for example, is described as the Ascot of the

Joe Sugden.

North, pretty Ripon is the Garden Course while Doncaster is known as Sunny Donny. Pontefract is the motorway course because of its location near the M62, while Wetherby is the A1 course because it is close to the Great North Road. Beverley is first past the post because it is quickly off the tapes with the flat season, Redcar is the family racecourse beside the sea and Catterick lies near a Roman village in the foothills of the Yorkshire Dales. The historic courses at Richmond and Hambleton closed long ago, while a recent closure was Stockton, later known as Teesside Park which was sited in the North Riding of Yorkshire.

Today's nine courses are spread throughout the three separate counties which comprise Yorkshire, i.e. North Yorkshire, West Yorkshire and South Yorkshire, but two of them are now outside the boundaries of the present county. In 1974, when local authority boundaries changed, two new counties were created on the borders of Yorkshire. One was Cleveland in the north which embraces Middlesbrough and Teesside – Redcar now lies within that area. The other is Humberside. Beverley, once the capital town of the East Riding of Yorkshire, is now within North Humberside, although the district has retained links with its former county by calling itself East Yorkshire.

In spite of these minor administrative differences, all nine racecourses consider themselves based in Yorkshire and publicize themselves as a group. The theme 'Go Racing in Yorkshire' embraces all nine, and at information centres and racecourses there are brochures and leaflets relating to them, with Family Days at most. Accompanied children under sixteen are admitted free and there is a range of additional entertainments including restaurants and bars. For beginners and those unaccustomed to the technicalities of horse racing, there is a free 'Beginner's Guide' which explains everything.

Joe obtained copies for Kate and the children because he wished to introduce them to the so-called Sport of Kings by taking them to one of the courses on a family day during the summer. But Kate is not so sure. She is not a racing fan and cannot understand the fervour with which Joe follows the horses. But he did persuade her to see for herself and promised that if she ever went to York with him on Ebor Day in August, he'd buy her a new outfit for the occasion. But first, they would go with Mark and Rachel and would start at a small course.

Joe selected Ripon, a charming, beautiful and well-situated course with a strong appeal to ladies. It lies a good mile from Ripon, which is one of Britain's smallest cities and is in picturesque surroundings between the River Ure and the Ripon Canal. The towering bulk of Ripon Cathedral provides a superb background to this oval-shaped course while the rolling countryside of lower Wensleydale and the Vale of Mowbray gives it a genuine rural aspect. The town is a jewel for it is rich with tradition and has a large market square where the Wakeman's Horn is still sounded at nine o'clock each evening by the Wakeman in his three-cornered hat.

The present racecourse is not Ripon's first, however, for there are few places which can boast as many racetracks. The city can boast a total of six and, indeed, Ripon was once the home of one of Henry VIII's studs. Racing took place on Bondgate Green as early as 1664, and on Monkton Moor in 1675, but it was a decision by the Municipal Corporation that led to the construction

Glamorous York Racecourse, known as the Ascot of the North and one of the finest courses in the country, is situated on the historic Knavesmire, the scene of public executions between 1379 and 1802. Once known as the Tyburn of York, it comprises a huge stretch of common land on the outskirts of the city; it was here on 7 April 1739 that a famous horseman ended his days. He was Dick Turpin, now buried in St George's Churchyard at York.

24

The beautiful cathedral city of Ripon has had six racecourses. The first was on Bondgate Green in 1664, while the first meeting on the present course was on 6 August 1900. Its race meetings are among the best in the north of England.

of a racecourse on High Common in 1714. When High Common was enclosed in 1826 as a result of the Enclosure Acts, this ended its days as a racecourse.

For the next ten years there was no racing in Ripon. Then a local publican called Haygarth encouraged racing on his own premises and this led to a new racecourse beside the River Ure. It operated until 1865 and was followed by yet another course on Red Banks which was bounded by the River Skell. When it closed, its grandstand became a school. The present track followed and the first meeting was held on 6 August 1900. But for more than 200 years, racing in Ripon was limited to only one annual meeting. This was in August and was the social event of the year at which the gentry entertained their guests and friends. This well-attended meeting was in honour of St Wilfred, the patron saint of Ripon who founded a monastery here and whose work led to the construction of the cathedral which is dedicated to him. The races were not held on his feast day for that is on 12 October, but the St Wilfred Handicap remains an important event on the Ripon race card.

The long history of Ripon City is honoured in other races including the Hornblower Stakes and the Ripon Rowell Stakes, the latter reminding us that years ago spurs or rowells were manufactured in the town. Their high quality led to a saying that men of great integrity were 'as true as Ripon rowells'. When James II came to Ripon he was presented with a pair of its famous spurs.

One innovation at Ripon occurred in 1723 with a race for lady jockeys. Although it drew large crowds, this did not please everyone for some thought it very unseemly. One very shocked spectator wrote: 'Nine of the sex rid astride, dressed in drawers and waistcoats and jockey caps, their shapes transparent. I think the lady benefactress to this indecent diversion should have made the tenth!'

Ripon's picturesque and progressive course has advanced to meet the continuing demands of racegoers, and its meetings now rank among the best in the north.

When Joe took Kate and the children, he selected a meeting in late July which was designated Children's Day. The course was bedecked with flowers; they adorned the paddock, the enclosures and even the grandstand, and perpetuated Ripon's claim to be one of the prettiest courses in England. For Kate, the colour and spectacle was exciting; there was glamour here, she decided, and money and style. There was the scent of success and the sound of happiness. She found herself looking at the ladies' fashions while Rachel admired the sleek horses as they paraded before each race. Mark, always wanting to know all there was to know about everything, tried to understand the hand-signals of the tic-tac men as they announced the odds for each runner. Joe explained how the odds shown on the bookmakers' boards were an indication of the expected result, stressing that nothing was certain and that experts can soon part with lots of money due to the vagaries of the sport. He explained the simple process of placing a bet – how to back a horse to win or gain a place.

He included the more sophisticated bets, some involving a succession of races on several courses. He added that some bookmakers on the course would not accept bets of less than £5 or those from youngsters under eighteen; if Mark wanted to place a bet, then Joe or Kate would do it for him.

While Joe was trying to explain all this to the youngsters, Kate wandered off. When Joe located her, she was standing at the window of the Tote building, placing a bet.

'What's she doing?' asked Mark.

'She's putting a bet on the Tote,' said Joe, explaining that this system was like a football pool. All the money placed on horses through the Tote (the Totalisator Board to give it its full name) was returned in prizes, less expenses. Here, you could place small stakes of £1 on horses either to win or to be placed, or you could attempt some of the more complex systems.

But when Kate came back, Joe asked, 'Well, which did you back?'

'Number four,' she smiled. 'To win.'

'Number four? What's its name?'

'I don't know,' she said. 'Does it matter?'

'You're supposed to study form,' he cried. 'You're supposed to see how well it's run before, whether it likes a course with left-hand bends or right hand bends, whether it likes the ground to be soft or hard, whether it's always lost before . . .'

'Oh, I just liked the look of it,' she said. 'I saw it going round and round that ring with the jockey on – and he smiled at me – so I thought I'd bet on it. Anyway, four is my lucky number!'

'Good old mum,' beamed Mark.

When they heard the announcer call 'weighed in', Joe took them to a vantage point on the rails and they saw number four gallop past. Joe looked at his race card and found it was called Cherryspink.

'That's the Yorkshire name for a hawfinch,' he said, 'but look, Kate, it's hardly rated in the bookies' minds. See, it's ten to one … that means they think it has a ten to one chance of winning, and that's not a lot! It's certainly not the favourite!'

'Oh, I don't understand all that,' she laughed. 'It's all a bit of fun …'

'It can be an expensive bit of fun if you're not careful,' cautioned Joe.

But as the runners were galloping up to the starter, Joe settled down to watch. The children stood at his side, leaning on the gleaming white rails as the starter held them steady. Then the tapes went up and the crowd roared, 'They're off!'

'Which one have you bet on?' Kate asked Joe.

'None,' he said. 'I was too busy explaining things to Mark and Rachel. I didn't have time!'

Kate now turned all her attention to the course. The field of eight beautiful horses and the jockeys' colourful silks provided a sea of brilliance, and as they reached the first bend they were all bunched together. Over the loudspeakers the commentator's voice provided the spectators with the current position.

'He mentioned mine!' shouted Kate.

'Aye, it's at the back of the field!' grinned Joe mischievously.

'No it's not!' she retorted. 'It's fifth and running well …'

'Aye, so it is, so let's hope it keeps that way …'

But as the field were taking the final bend, Cherryspink was overtaking the others … he was running second now … on the outside … coming fast …

The commentator was growing excited. 'It's Cherryspink,' he was shouting. 'Neck and neck with Grosvenor … Cherryspink making the running, Cherryspink all the way … and as they come to the line it's Cherryspink … Cherryspink wins … Grosvenor second … River Wharfe third. First, Number 4, second number 2, third number 6 …'

'I've won, I've won!' shouted Kate, flinging her arms around Joe and jumping up and down with excitement. There was fuss and movement now, the crowd was babbling and chattering too and the spectators were drifting back to the bars, back to the information boards and, in some cases, back to the Tote building.

'What do I do now?' she asked, bubbling with delight.

'You wait until the Tote has calculated the amount of payout to the winners, then you take your ticket back and collect your winnings.'

'My ticket? Where is it? What did I do with it? Joe, did I give it to you …'

'No you didn't! It'll be in your handbag, among all that other rubbish you cart around …'

Kate found it and was paid £15.40 pence for her win, the Tote's prices differing slightly from those of the course bookies.

'Oh, Joe, what a tonic! I could get to like this.'

Cantering to the start at Wetherby.

'Just remember you don't win every time,' he laughed and kissed her as they all went to have a look at the runners in the next race.

On the way home in the car, Kate was beaming with her new-found wealth, having won a total of £24.65p while Joe was feeling sorry for himself, having lost £8, as well as having to pay the cost of entry and the occasional refreshment between races. But it had been a pleasant and entertaining day's outing, especially for the children. Rachel had won £2 and Mark finished even, thanks to Joe's advice, and as they drove back to Emmerdale he explained more about racing in Yorkshire.

'In the winter,' he said, 'there is very little flat racing. Instead, it's the tradition that horses race over fences like they do in the Grand National. They are called National Hunt meetings or steeplechases. Years ago, some fox hunters decided to race each other in a straight line across the countryside to a distant church steeple. They had to jump fences and hedges and gallop across fields, so National Hunt meetings are still called steeplechases.

'Wetherby is the only course in Yorkshire devoted entirely to that kind of racing. There is no flat racing there. In fact, Wetherby Racecourse is, and always has been, the home of jumping in Yorkshire, the focal point of National Hunt racing and one of the country's finest National Hunt courses. They've been jumping over fences in this area since the 1840s. There used to be a course at Linton on the banks of the River Wharfe but the rent became too expensive and so the Race Committee found another site – that's where we've just been. That course was established in 1891 and the first meeting was at Easter that year.'

'But they do race over hurdles on other courses, don't they?' asked Kate.

'Oh aye, in Yorkshire they jump at Catterick and Doncaster but only in the winter. Then in summer it's the turn of the flat season.'

'But I've seen them jumping at the same time as they're racing on the flat!' commented Mark.

'Aye, the seasons can overlap, a bit like the football and cricket seasons. But in Yorkshire we try to end the National Hunt season in March so the flat racing begins in April; then the flat season ends in September or October when the National Hunt resumes. But there are overlaps – at Sunny Donny, for example, you can get flat and National Hunt races at the same meeting, perhaps spread over three days, and also at Doncaster you can get flat racing into November while Wetherby is busy with National Hunt meetings. By the way, Kate, at Sunny Donny, there's a special Ladies' Stand with its own dining and bar facilities.'

'I always thought Yorkshiremen didn't welcome women who wanted to join their sports and pastimes!'

'So now you know differently, eh? Anyroad, Doncaster is one of the best courses in the country, some reckon it's better than York, even if the town isn't particularly glamorous! Doncaster racecourse is on Town Moor – there was racing in the town as long ago as 1595 but this course became established about 1751. It was called the Doncaster Horse Course.'

'Isn't there a famous race at Doncaster?'

'There are several,' Joe told her. 'The Lincoln Handicap for example, but you're probably thinking of the St Leger. That's the oldest classic race in England, it started at Doncaster in 1776.'

'St Leger? That's a funny name for a saint!' chuckled Mark.

'It's not a saint!' Joe grinned. 'It's named after Lieutenant Colonel Anthony St Leger who, in 1776, suggested a sweepstake of 25 guineas each for three-year-old horses. You're too young to know what a guinea was; it was £1.1s which is £1.5p in today's cash. It was a lot of money then. Anyroad, his first race was in 1777, but wasn't given a name – but a year later it was named in his honour and the St Leger is now one of the country's top classics. It's the highlight of the flat season in Doncaster. Way back in 1892, 173 full trains brought racegoers to see this race – it attracted the best horses in the world and some of the most eminent people. In its early days that meeting, in September, lasted a whole week. Now it's for four days in September, but it's still called the St Leger Festival and there's still a tremendous atmosphere with marquees and all the trappings of a top event.'

As they drove home, Joe explained how he enjoyed his visits to Thirsk, the small but friendly racecourse which is so close to the centre of that North Yorkshire market town. It wasn't far from the NY Estate office he used to visit. With its fine cobbled marketplace, old coaching inns and quaint streets, Thirsk is a pleasant town and Joe often found himself walking around the quiet areas, beside Cod Beck or through the back alleys to the old town.

He then told them about Catterick racecourse, once called Catterick Bridge to distinguish it from nearby Catterick Camp which is a huge military base.

The racecourse lies at the end of Catterick Village where the A1 used to form the main street. In fact, the A1 ran beside the final straight and cars could keep pace with the galloping horses. Today, the A1 bypass has allowed Catterick to become a peaceful village even if there is an RAF Regiment

There has been racing in Doncaster since 1595, but the present racecourse, first known as Doncaster Horse Course, was established on Town Moor around 1751. The course hosts the St Leger, the oldest classic race in England.

depot there. It was near the racecourse that the ancient Roman village of Cataractonium was discovered, and the route of a Roman road runs immediately to the west of the racetrack where it forms the path of the bypass. In Saxon times, Catterick was very important due to its strategic position on the north-south routes. The bridge over the River Swale is opposite the racecourse entrance close to the Catterick Bridge Hotel and it has witnessed travellers of five centuries, including kings and queens, stage coaches and motor cars, racegoers and visitors to England who have trekked from as far north as Scotland.

Joe then began to relate some curious tales about the course at Catterick. He said it was a local farmers' course, although it was patronised by yeomen, huntsmen, county types and gentry alike from Swaledale and Wensleydale, as well as others from Durham, Northumberland and even Scotland. It opened on 22 April 1783, although there was racing in the village a century and a half earlier, and within fifty years or so it became regarded as a very fashionable course even though its early facilities were non-existent or, at the best, rather primitive.

A grandstand was built in 1906 and has not changed since! It is very much a countryman's course; set in a small village surrounded by open countryside, the nearest town of any size is Darlington whose people once showed little interest in the sport. Rather surprisingly, it is one of the most popular courses and one of the busiest tracks in the country.

'Instead of cash prizes,' he told Kate, 'they used to race for a pipe of claret or port – a pipe is 126 gallons, by the way! At that time, there was no entry fee for the course – that was introduced in 1888. Certainly it lacked finesse but everyone found it enjoyable. Apart from the official races, there would sometimes be private contests between individuals and it seems these were

Thirsk Racecourse, one of the most popular in the north east of England, is on land where the Bell family, squires of Thirsk, used to exercise their horses. At one stage the racehorses were stabled at several inns within the town which are within easy walking distance of the track.

Beverley Racecourse. In 1690 Beverley Corporation gave permission for a horse-race course to be established on 1,100 acres of town land known as Beverley Westwood. That course is still in use and celebrated its 300th anniversary on 22 September 1990.

very popular. One clerk of the course said his only expenses were a barrel of tar and a sack of feathers to be used on any bookmaker caught welshing – those who were caught were also thrown into the River Swale. Welshing is when a bookmaker runs off with his takings instead of paying out the winnings. Another entertainment was to turn a stag loose on the course and show off the skills of the local hunt by organising a chase but it was a farmer who saved the day on one memorable occasion!'

'What happened?' asked Mark, full of interest.

'It had snowed overnight,' Joe told him. 'The course was inches deep and racing was impossible. But it was an important meeting and to abandon it would have cost a lot of people a lot of money.

'Now, we farmers are known for our ability to overcome problems like that and so the landlord of the Catterick Bridge Hotel, who was also a farmer and whose name was Thomas Ferguson, came up with an idea. Before racing started, he drove a flock of sheep round and round the course until the deep snow was reduced to a mere covering. And so the meeting went ahead.'

Over the final miles to Emmerdale, Joe told them about Beverley Races on their famous Westwood course; in its early days, Beverley Corporation charged the Race Committee 6d (2½p) rent because it supported racing on the 1,100 acres of town property. Indeed, the whole area around Beverley was noted for its breeding of bloodstock as well as its country pursuits which included horse racing, coursing and other greyhound events. These were attended by nationally respected trainers, jockeys and owners. The course celebrated its 300th anniversary on 22 September 1990, for it was on that date in 1690 that the Corporation's Great Order Book read, 'Liberty is given to make a convenient ground on the Westwood for a horse race, the surveyors to appoint posts to be used on that behalf.'

Years ago, during Beverley's raceweek in summer, there was held on the Sunday a football match between Beverley and the surrounding villages. This took place through the streets. On one noted occasion in the early 1800s, the local butcher kicked the ball over the North Bar and a mêlée ensued. The church was invaded and other premises damaged by those chasing the ball.

Then a man found it and jumped on his horse to escape with it; the constable tried to stop him being attacked and was himself knocked unconscious with a stone and the outcome was that a massive riot broke out. The mayor and forty militia were summoned; the mayor read the Riot Act as the soldiers fixed bayonets and that was the end of the annual football match.

But the racecourse is not the only venue for local horse racing. One of the oldest races in the world is run nearby, this being the famous Kiplingcotes Derby. Founded by a party of fox-hunters, it runs a four-mile course across the Yorkshire Wolds, starting in the parish of Etton and finishing in the parish of Middleton-on-the-Wolds. If the race lapses for just one year, it will cease, but it has been run every year since 1619. In 1947, when heavy snow made it impossible, the farmers walked their horses around the course, just to continue the tradition. The founders left a sum of money to provide a fund for the winner, and the man who comes second gets the stake money. Thus the rider who is second invariably gets more than the winner!

Joe admitted he had not been to Pontefract many times, although the course was pleasant enough even if its industrial surroundings were less than salubrious. They include Ferrybridge Cooling Towers, the M62, and a colliery with shale heaps and smoke. But the town itself is most famous for liquorice sweets known as Pontefract Cakes.

It does, however, have many historic landmarks. Its castle was the last royalist stronghold to capitulate during the Civil War. But not even that event halted the local horse racing. In 1648 a Captain Adam Baynes wrote to his brother to announce that racing would be held within fourteen days of Candlemas Day (2 February) and he asked whether his brother's horse would be running. History was repeated when another war featured in Pontefract's racing history – along with Stockton, these were the only northern courses where racing was allowed during World War II.

At Redcar, Joe went on, which is the home of the world's oldest lifeboat, the Zetland, and where the bathing machine was invented, the first races took place on the sands, one of which was a contest between horses and foxhounds. There was chaos once when the wind blew away the hounds' trail. The last race on the sandy beach was around 1870 and the present course opened in August 1872. It is one of only two courses in England with a completely straight length of 1 mile 1 furlong. (The other is Newmarket.) It became famous for its 'good stakes, good horses and good patronage' and is known as a track where the going is always described as good. On 5 August 1986 HRH

Redcar Racecourse is near the coast. It is one of only two in England with a completely straight length of one mile and one furlong. Before this course was built, racing took place on the beach and some contests were between race horses and foxhounds.

Princess Anne rode a winner here called Gulfland. Kate said she had no intention of emulating that lady.

They arrived home in a happy mood, the children enthusing about their day out and Kate still beaming about her winnings. She thanked Joe with a kiss and confirmed that one day she'd love to visit York Races.

During the summer, when that wish had slipped from his mind, Kate presented him with a large but lightweight parcel.

'What is it?' He felt it; it was soft and light, but unwieldy in its large bag. He opened the covering to find a brown trilby hat.

'A trilby?' he was bemused. 'What's this for?'

'For you,' she said. 'I bought it with my winnings at Ripon. Practically all the racing men I saw were wearing brown trilby hats, so I thought you should have one.'

'Thanks,' he kissed her and put it on, and laughed. 'So when do I show it off?'

'How about the Ebor Meeting at York?' she said, tilting her chin in her characteristic way.

'You're on!' he chuckled, gathering her in his arms – and then he remembered *his* promise to buy her a new outfit!

Henry in the dales

WHEN Henry Wilks took early retirement from his career as a wool dyer in Bradford, he decided to live in a Yorkshire dales village. He had lost his wife and, having spent so much time in a city environment, wanted a new life with time to spend on his leisure interests. These included exploration of the Yorkshire countryside combined with the study of nature. His special interest is wild birds, particularly those of the Pennine region, and in order to gain peace and tranquillity to observe them he chose the isolated village of Beckindale as his new home. His early hopes were dashed, however, when his splendid house, Inglebrook, suffered irreparable damage from an unfortunate fire and so Henry made his temporary home at the Woolpack Inn – and he liked it so much that he has been there ever since.

Having injected some much-needed cash into the business, he became a partner and so joined the resident licensee and proprietor, Amos Brearly, in running and managing the renowned Woolpack. After more than a decade as a partner, and even though the two of them are firm friends, Amos continues to address Henry very formally as 'Mr Wilks'!

It is one of Henry's joys to serve behind the bar where he meets the people of Beckindale and from this he has become a loved and respected member of the community. Nonetheless, he still likes to get away from the pressures of business, so when he gets time off he heads for the dales and high fells within the Yorkshire Dales National Park. There he can feel the bracing wind upon his face and the spring of the turf beneath his feet. Armed with a pair of binoculars, a notebook, some weatherproof clothing and a picnic lunch, he happily spends hours in the countryside as he studies the birds that have made their home in that glorious landscape.

One of his favourite places is Littlewell, some eight miles north-east of Hotten. This is the site of the Littlewell Nature Reserve which has some miniature lakes, lush woodland and marshy areas which together support a renowned collection of rare orchids and a variety of wild birds. One of the orchids is the lady's slipper, once thought to be extinct in Yorkshire, while among the rare birds that Henry has recorded here have been a Cetti's warbler, a red-backed shrike and a golden oriole.

Henry Wilks.

Malham Cove, a natural amphitheatre with a cliff face over 240 feet high. A stream bubbles from beneath the cliff and it was here that Charles Kingsley received the inspiration to write The Water Babies. *According to legend, there is a five-fold echo from one particular point near the Cove.*

It was a visit to Malham Cove when he was a child that whetted his appetite for the wild fells and their birds. Even now, he can recall that visit – he was twelve at the time. While walking with his parents across the expanse of moorland between Malham Cove and Malham Tarn, he heard the simultaneous singing of the skylark and the curlew. Each bird's lyrics complemented the other in a most remarkable fashion and there was the glorious sound of the open air in their music. From that moment, he has associated their songs with the moors and dales.

The skylark is a mottled brown bird which is slightly larger than a house sparrow and across the years it has charmed the poets and song writers with its music. It rises vertically and sometimes disappears from view where it sings in the heavens with a light, warbling voice. Then it will return to earth, dropping swiftly and bursting into more song as it approaches the ground. Henry loves the skylark, which is known as the laverock to Yorkshire people, for it epitomises all that is wild and free.

Something like half a century has passed since Henry's first sight of Malham, but he still visits it whenever he can. It is now the centre for many dales walks, most of them enjoying spectacular surrounds. The village, comprising a few sturdy stone cottages beside a stream, was once a sleepy place, but now it is busy with tourists. There is a recently constructed footpath from the village to the remarkable Malham Cove, a natural amphitheatre with an astonishing pale limestone cliff as its backcloth. This is over 240 feet high and is one of the striking sights of Yorkshire. There is a legend that from one particular place within that cove there is a five-fold echo, but Henry has never heard it.

36

From beneath the cliff of Malham Cove, a stream arises apparently from the depths of the earth to flow crystal clear towards the village – this is the infant River Aire. It probably seeps from Malham Tarn which lies in the fells above the cove, its waters finding their way through the limestone to emerge in this magical way. It was here that Charles Kingsley received the inspiration to write *The Water Babies*.

The village is beautiful, but the walk to the cove is dramatic and the National Park authority has constructed a flight of steps up the side of the cove. The climb is worth every aching limb; indeed, it forms part of the Pennine Way, Britain's longest footpath. This is 250 miles long and crosses these hills to provide staggering vistas. On top of the cove, the terrain becomes a curious plateau comprising huge pieces of limestone rock which are riddled with hollows. These are known as clints and grykes – the clints are the rocks and the grykes are the hollows between them; the hollows are reminders that this is caving country. Beneath the surrounding hills are massive caverns with underground streams, lakes and waterfalls; one of them is Gaping Ghyll, the largest limestone cavern in Britain whose main chamber is large enough to accommodate York Minster. But Henry Wilks has never ventured underground – he prefers to walk above it all!

Henry has often walked across the clints and grykes, following the Pennine Way or the other footpaths. One of them leads along the foot of Ing Scar and climbs Comb Hill, but all lead towards Malham Tarn. This lonely moorland lake, about half a mile in diameter, offers its own nature reserve along its western shores as well as a nature trail near the Field Centre on the northern shore. Among the Tarn's visitors have been Charles Darwin, John Ruskin and William Wordsworth, and it is here that the curlew wheels in the sky during the summer months, often moving to the coast in winter. With its mottled brown plumage, this is Europe's largest wading bird and is so easily identified with its downward curving beak. It breaks into a bubbling, trilling song as it flies over its breeding grounds on these moors. A villager once told Henry

A Canada Goose, one of many species sometimes seen around Malham Tarn. The bird is also seen in parklands and gardens, and even in the wild it is too tame to be regarded as a target for wildfowlers. The bird was introduced to this country from Canada especially to adorn parklands and is now present in the wild throughout the year.

Dry-stone walls form intricate patterns throughout the Yorkshire Dales. Built centuries ago, they create boundaries, barriers and shelter but they do require regular maintenance. Here, a dry stone wall has just been repaired by a sturdy fellow from the Dales.

that the local people believe it will rain if the curlew is heard at night, but for some the crying of a curlew at night used to be regarded as a herald of death. Our forefathers could not see what was making those human-like cries of anguish high in the night sky and thought it was the Seven Whistlers, souls whose weird calls foretold a local or family disaster.

The Tarn is one of several inland waters within the Pennine dales, and is a refuge for all kinds of wildlife. In the late spring and summer months, Henry has noticed sandpipers here, as well as the occasional snipe. These love to explore the higher reaches of the streams known in Yorkshire as gills or becks.

Both birds will cheerfully nest on these remote fells. The sandpiper arrives from Africa in April and remains until October, but it is not easy to notice among the rocks of these becks and gills; it is easier to spot on the shores of the Tarn. Less than eight inches long, it has dark-brown upper parts and white underparts which merge with the background so that it becomes almost invisible. It has a long beak and legs and runs along with a crouching gait, inspecting the shores and damp patches for grubs. Sometimes it whizzes along a river, skimming low over the water in a gliding flight while uttering the piping call from which it gets its name.

The snipe is a bird which always amuses Henry. Its huge beak is almost a quarter of the bird's entire length and, like the curlew and the sandpiper, this is a wading bird who loves the tarns and becks. But the enormous beak is the snipe's lifesaver for the tip is very sensitive and is used to locate and identify the various grubs and worms upon which it feeds. It seeks them by probing deep into the mud although it will enjoy titbits obtained from the surface. The snipe has another odd habit – during its courtship it will fly high into the sky and then dive back to earth with its tail feathers spread wide. This produces a strange bleating sound and when the snipe has completed this stunt it will fly back into the sky and do it all over again.

There are other birds at Malham Tarn, too, such as the red grouse, black-headed gulls, swallows in the summer and passing wild geese in the winter. Some birds come for the fishing! The monks of Fountains Abbey once fished here, but angling is now strictly controlled and Henry made a note to remind Alan Turner of that!

One of Henry's favourite walks from Malham Tarn takes him a mile or so to the west from where he picks up the footpath which leads through Gordale Scar. It is about a mile from the Tarn via the footpath. This terminates way below in Malham village, and offers an awesome sight for Gordale Scar is said to be Yorkshire's modest answer to the Grand Canyon. The footpath down this huge gap in the hills can be treacherous and Henry always ensures he is wearing adequate footwear. Gordale Scar is a deep ravine with roaring water-falls; Gordale Beck crashes some 300 feet in twin falls as the towering cliffs adopt weird shapes and outlines which, at night, would be capable of frightening the calmest of visitors. It is a weird place at times, almost eerie in some lights. Wordsworth was impressed with it, describing it as 'Gordale chasm, terrific as the lair where the young lions crouch,' while other writers have described the chasm as dreadful or a horror where loose stones on towering cliffs threaten idle spectators with instant destruction! But they were Victorian writers with an eye for the melodramatic; in truth it is a place of awesome fascination and natural splendour albeit requiring care during exploration.

Wild goats once roamed this area; Henry has never seen any in modern times, although goats do live wild in remote parts of Northumberland and Cumbria.

It is the birds of prey that here fascinate Henry Wilks. He has long been intrigued by hawks, harriers, buzzards and eagles for this is their ideal country. It has long been his ambition to see a golden eagle in the higher dales and although he has seen them in Scotland and near Haweswater in the Lake District not many miles away across the Pennines, he has yet to sight one within the Dales National Park. Reports have reached him, however, of such sightings, a positive one being some twenty years ago in 1970, shortly before he settled in Beckindale. Of the other sightings, Henry believes these supposed 'eagles' might have been buzzards. Although the golden eagle is a massive size, almost three feet in length with a wing span of around eight feet, the buzzard can appear equally massive when viewed from the ground.

The golden eagle, as the name suggests, is a beautiful golden brown colour, and when it soars aloft its wing tips look like extended fingers. The sheer power of the eagle is such that it can lift and fly with something as large as a fox, although hares, rabbits and game birds are its most usual prey. By comparison, the buzzard is small at a mere two feet or so in length, probably less in most cases. It soars and glides in the air, often with a soft mewing cry which is a distinguishing feature and buzzards can be seen around Malham and Gordale. So, too, can peregrine falcons, those dive-bombers from the heavens. Wheeling aloft as it looks out for its prey, the peregrine falcon suddenly folds its wings and drops like a stone at speeds of up to 180 miles an

The golden eagle is rare in the Yorkshire Dales, the last positive sighting being in 1970. The golden eagle has a massive wing span of almost eight feet (2.5 metres), and it has been recorded in the Lake District to the west of the Dales.

hour. It hunts other birds in mid-air, striking a victim with its talons and instantly breaking its neck.

Hovering kestrels, dashing sparrowhawks and tiny merlins have all been spotted by Henry Wilks in his rambles around the dales of the Craven region but one of his two most memorable sightings was of a male hen harrier, a pale grey hunter with black wing tips which earned its name from its habit, years ago, of preying on domestic fowl. He watched a pair at their nest – the hen was sitting and the male called to her; he was carrying a tiny bird which he had caught and so she left the nest and flew to him. He rose above her and dropped the catch as she twisted to fly upside down for a second, catching the falling prey in her own claws.

Henry's other sighting was of that scarcest of birds, the osprey. It paid a visit to a Yorkshire lake which he refuses to identify for fear that someone might attempt to kill the bird should it return. It is a large eagle-like bird of prey with dark-grey upper parts and white underparts and it survives on a diet of fish. It is a rare visitor to England. He saw it one autumn morning when it broke its journey from Scotland to Africa.

To catch its prey, this magnificent bird hovers high above the water, then plunges down and crashes feet first into the water to emerge with its prey between its claws.

The Yorkshire Dales National Park embraces some of England's finest and most spectacular scenery, including many lonely fells and lofty mountains of the Pennine range. Among them are the Three Peaks, Whernside, Ingleborough and Penyghent, all over 2,200 feet high. Pictured here is Ingleborough which is 2,373 feet high (723 metres), the second highest of the peaks. Whernside is the highest at 2,414 feet (736 metres).

In his leisure moments, Henry explores the whole range of the Yorkshire Dales National Park, a huge area of countryside which embraces some of England's finest and most spectacular scenery. Among its major features are Yorkshire's great rivers, four of which flow down the broad dales of Wensleydale, Swaledale, Nidderdale and Wharfedale. There are hundreds of smaller dales too, all rich with isolated communities and wild life. There are lofty fells with mountains like the three peaks, Whernside, Ingleborough and Penyghent all of which are over 2,200 feet high, and scenic wonders like Brimham Rocks, the Buttertubs, tarns and crags galore, inland lakes like Semerwater, and waterfalls like those at Ingleton and Hardraw Force. There are gardens to visit and brass band concerts to enjoy, woods to explore and canals to stroll beside. For the adventurous there are massive underground caves and for the placid there are museums, castles, country houses and historic buildings to admire. Within the dales there are some delightful market towns like Grassington, Ingleton, Sedburgh, Hawes, Skipton, Leyburn, Settle, Richmond and Pateley Bridge, with larger towns like Harrogate, Huddersfield, Bradford, Leeds and Wakefield within easy reach.

Henry likes to visit places such as Bainbridge with its quaint horn-blowing ceremony. This occurs on the village green every evening as it has for the last 700 years. There is Richmond with its Georgian theatre, its castle and cobbled market place, Middleham and its links with Richard III, Dent and Grassington with their lovely old streets, Ilkley with its famous moor, and Appletreewick which is as pretty as its name implies. There are hundreds of square miles of open countryside, hundreds of dales and hundreds of villages, each with distinctive and sturdy Yorkshire characteristics, cosy inns and friendly people.

One of Henry's favourite places, high in Wensleydale, is Aysgarth with its densely wooded slopes and tumbling waterfalls which extend for more than half a mile down the River Ure. Standing above them, as if on guard, is a splendid parish church with a prized fifteenth-century rood screen. It overlooks an old cotton mill reputed to have made the red shirts for Garibaldi's army; Garibaldi was an Italian soldier whose army of Red Shirts conquered Sicily and Naples in 1860.

The best time to experience the real splendour of Aysgarth Falls is during the winter when the river is full of fresh water, much of which comes from

Richmond is the capital town of Swaledale. With cobbled streets, steep and narrow alleys, and a huge cobbled market place, it retains an air of medieval calm. Rich with historic relics, from its own castle and the nearby abbey at Easby, it is popular with visitors and makes an ideal centre for touring the northern Yorkshire Dales. One of its famous daughters was Frances l'Anson, and when song writer Leonard MacNally fell in love with her, he wrote his famous song 'The Lass of Richmond Hill'.

43

Middleham is one of the most historic villages in the Yorkshire Dales. On the slopes of Wensleydale, it has two market places, some steep streets and old crosses, all in the shadows of the imposing castle which was owned by Richard III. His son, Edward Prince of Wales, was born and died here in 1484 at the age of eight.

melted snow on the fells. It roars through the trees and crashes down a succession of high steps as it races down the wide dale over massive grey rocks and down yet more cascades which form a giant staircase.

Overlooking the river in this tiny village is The Yorkshire Museum of Carriages with a Mountain Rescue Post and National Park Information Centre nearby, but Henry likes to walk beside the river. This takes him through the woods beside the waterfalls and there he can seek his precious wild birds.

In the woods Henry has noticed a variety of birds that one might see in the garden: chaffinches, greenfinches and bullfinches, robins, wrens, blackbirds and thrushes, jackdaws, rooks, tawny owls and marauding magpies, but from time to time he hears the laughing call of the yaffle or the green woodpecker as it is formally known.

Henry knows that some townsfolk often think this is an escaped parrot, so bright are its colours. It has a vivid green back and wings, a yellow rump, black wing tips and tail, and a bright scarlet crown to its head. The male has a red moustache, too. Its laughing cry is a ready indication of its presence and this colourful bird nests in a hollow in an old tree trunk. There are other woodpeckers hereabouts, like the black-and-white great spotted woodpecker and the rarer lesser spotted woodpecker, all of whom make use of hollow trees for their nests. Sometimes the drumming sounds of a woodpecker at work, busily pecking at a tree stump, can be heard from the woodland paths.

The clean river enables one to see a dipper at work. Rather like a large wren, the dipper is smaller than a blackbird but bigger than a robin. With very dark-brown upper parts, it looks almost black and an old Yorkshire name for it was the water blackbird. But unlike the blackbird it has a very white chest with a ruddy bib below; it is a kind of chestnut coloured cumberbund. It has a short stumpy tail and a habit of flexing its legs as it stands upon a stone.

When standing on a rock in the river, it will constantly dip and bow, bobbing up and down while the water rushes past. When it offers to sing, it produces a delightful warbling song which can be heard above the roar of the water.

But this bird, even though it does not have the webbed feet of ducks, geese and swans, does swim well; indeed, sometimes it appears to prefer a swim to a flight, and it has another odd skill. It can walk underwater. When Henry first witnessed this trick, he was amazed for it would seem that such a bouyant bird would never be able to remain beneath the surface. But, as if by magic, the dipper can. Although when swimming it bobs along like a cork, it can also take a leisurely stroll along the river bed in search of food. It seems to stay beneath the surface because it puts its head down, folds its wings tight against its body and allows the flowing water to add pressure to its back; this helps it stay on the river bed for as long as a full minute where it seeks its small prey such as insects, worms and even tadpoles.

In the dales the dipper is plentiful, preferring the rugged country with fast flowing streams, and consequently it is not very common in the flat regions.

Another exciting sight along the Yorkshire rivers is the brilliantly coloured kingfisher. Predominantly blue and red with dashes of green, black and white, this tiny, fast-flying bird speeds up and down the river with a piercing cry. It is a shy bird, and consequently Henry knows that he must find a quiet place away from the regular haunts of visitors if he is to see this beauty. Because some northern rivers freeze in the winter, denying the kingfisher its daily food, it moves to the coast and fishes in the sea, but it returns as soon as it can. It will sit on a small bough overhanging the water until it spots a minnow, then it will dive headlong into the water to catch the unwary fish. And this is when nature is so cruel because it kills the fish by beating its head against the branch, then swallows it head first.

A short stretch of Aysgarth Falls seen in the summer. In the winter months the river is full of fresh water, and these falls, which extend for a mile and a half downstream, provide a spectacular sight.

A view of Wharfedale with snow-capped peaks.

Henry had great pride, after an outing to Aysgarth, in educating Amos Brearly about the kingfisher's place in the Greek legends.

'They call it the halcyon,' Henry told him. 'The legend tells of Ceyx, the son of the day star, and Halcyone, the daughter of the god of the winds. When Ceyx was drowned during a shipwreck, and Halcyone drowned herself in grief, the gods took pity and changed the couple into kingfishers. For fourteen days in the winter, when Halcyone broods on her nest, her father, Aeolus, causes the winds to cease and this makes the sea calm so that she can complete her family. Halcyon, in Greek, means the 'brooding on the sea', and for us, halcyon days are days of happiness and calm. Like when I go to Aysgarth.'

'Shakespeare said summat about halcyon days,' grunted Amos, not wishing to be out-classed by Henry's literary knowledge.

'And so did Dryden,' beamed Henry. 'He said, and I quote,

Amidst our arms as quiet you shall be
As halcyons brooding on a winter's sea.'

Henry Wilks has discovered many footpaths beside the River Ure in Wensleydale. They stretch upstream and down, one of them following the line of the river via Redmire Force down to Wensley Bridge. It is Henry's delight to explore these, sometimes venturing as high as Bolton Castle to the north or into remote Coverdale to the south of the river.

But one of his favourite trips is to drive across the fells into Swaledale. Of the several routes, he likes the lonely, elevated route via the Buttertubs Pass; these are deep shafts in the limestone which were formed by acidic water enlarging ancient holes and they lie close to the summit of the pass. This route links Hawes in Wensleydale with Muker in Swaledale via Thwaite and the drive offers breathtaking views.

Before reaching Muker, Henry's route carries him into Thwaite and then Keld, and a few yards beyond Keld his route branches into Stonesdale. This astonishing lonely road carries him high into the Pennines because a few miles along here is England's highest pub. It is called Tan Hill Inn and is 1,732 feet above sea level. It commands superb views over the hills and dales of North Yorkshire and South Durham, with Cumbria in the near distance. This is some of the most wild and untamed landscape in England, weatherbeaten and remote but well worth the effort. Years ago, coal was mined on these heights and the buildings of the pub were once offices for that enterprise; now, they provide shelter for travellers just as they have for centuries, although the motor car has made this famous inn reasonably accessible.

On a hot summer day, it is one of Henry's greatest pleasures to sit upon a flat rock behind the inn, with a long cool pint of beer at his side and gaze across the vast emptiness. But for him, the moors are never empty, they are never deserted for here is bird life in abundance.

The lovely wheatear is one visitor, and for the people of this region it is a herald of spring. It arrives in March or early April from Africa and spends the summer on the Yorkshire fells where it rears a brood of up to seven youngsters who mature to join their parents upon the long trip back to Africa in October.

The pastel colours of the wheatear are soft and beautiful. With a slate blue/grey head and shoulders, the male has a white rump and tail, although there is a distinctive black T mark on the tail. The underparts are a soft yellow with white edges and he has a prominent black stripe across his eyes and cheeks. His partner has a greenish-brown back with buff underparts, but she does have the black T mark on her tail. They love the open wastelands of North Yorkshire, nesting under boulders and finding their food in the insects, larvae and centipedes that flourish in these parts.

But it was back at the Woolpack, another famous Yorkshire inn, that Amos Brearly tried to put Henry to the test by asking which was his favourite bird.

'All of 'em,' grinned Henry. 'I like 'em all, even the greedy starling or the cheeky sparrow!'

'But there must be one who you like better than all t'others, Mr Wilks?'

'The wren is a real gentleman, Amos, even if he is called Jenny Wren!'

'How do you make that out?'

'Did you know, Amos, that the cock wren will build up to eight nests every spring for his lady love to examine? He strives for perfection, you see, and she inspects them all, one by one, rejecting every one until she finds the right one! Now, if you've seen the work that goes into a wren's nest, you'll understand what that means.'

'She sounds a bit finicky to me, Mr Wilks.'

'Selective, Amos. She knows what she wants, you see, so when she likes one of them, she will line it with cosy feathers and wool. She makes it into a real love nest.'

'Aye, well, I can understand you liking a chap with that sort of patience, Mr Wilks.'

'There's another reason, Amos.'

'What's that?'

'He sings with a Yorkshire accent!' laughed Henry.

4

Dolly by the sea

WHEN Dolly Acaster was a small girl living in Darlington, one of her delights was to be taken by her mother or aunt to play on the sands. The beaches along the east coast, known locally as sands, were always beautifully soft and golden, none more so than the splendid Yorkshire stretches. There was, and still is, a wide choice which includes Redcar, Saltburn, Sandsend, Whitby, Scarborough, Filey and Bridlington. Even if the wind was a 'bit sharp' or if the water of the North Sea with its famous white horses was 'a bit on the chilly side' as her mother would say, the happiness of those days continued to live in her memory.

When she grew up and obtained work in the Woolpack Inn, Beckindale, she found romance, too. She married Matt Skilbeck and it was the birth of young Sam in 1983 that revived Dolly's childhood love of the seaside. His arrival meant that Dolly, with Matt at her side, could re-live those happy times with her very own family. She could help young Sam to build sand castles or laugh with him as he tried to jump across the incoming waves while the sea-water tickled his toes. For a few years, therefore, Dolly, Matt and Sam visited Bridlington and Scarborough for their holidays – but since her separation from Matt, Dolly often now goes alone. She does take little Sam whenever she can but there are times when he is at school and she has time off work, and so from time to time she drives across the hills to explore her old haunts.

Bridlington, on the coast of East Yorkshire, remains one of her regular calls because it is within such easy reach of Beckindale. From time to time she walks unobserved along the sands or the promenades, sometimes with Sam and sometimes alone. She will settle on a seat and gaze out to sea as if hoping that some impossible dream might come true.

Sometimes she will play on the sands with Sam, helping him build a castle, and sometimes she will just walk around the town. With its fascinating mixture of old streets and new, its exhilarating promenades, its twin piers like a pair of protective arms, the sweep of the bay with the cliffs behind and the array of flowers that adorn the town centre, Dolly has happy memories of being on holiday here with Matt. She recalls her family being together in the tiny flat

overlooking the harbour with its fish quay and flotilla of colourful small boats, and she remembers how she and Matt showed Sam how to use a bucket and spade as the gulls cried and wheeled above.

Dolly Skilbeck.

Bridlington is on the coast of East Yorkshire. It was once a small village but is now a popular holiday town. It has a range of old and new streets, a fine beach, a beautiful bay overlooked by impressive cliffs, and a colourful harbour.

When she comes alone, she explores the town away from the foreshore, admiring the priory that Annie had once shown her, exploring the shops and restaurants or just watching the wide range of ships that use the harbour or steam along the horizon. Beyond the harbour, the bay often seems so calm – indeed it is known as the Bay of Safety to sea-faring men – but when the wind is from the north or the north east, waves come crashing towards the shore and batter the sea wall to send fountains of spray high into the air. Within the shelter of the harbour, there are smaller vessels – trawlers, fishing cobles, yachts and pleasure boats, all able to find space and it makes Dolly realise that Bridlington harbour is a place of work for many people.

This is especially so for the fishermen, even if visitors do regard the scene as attractive and fascinating. There are boat races in the bay, too, while in the nearby gardens there is a seventeenth-century sundial; close to the north pier is another sundial which seems to be observing the ships that constantly pass, for it bears the legend: 'So passeth the glory of the world.'

For Dolly, the harbour activity is of constant interest. One day she watched the hoisting of the storm cone on the south pier; this indicates gales and storms and she learned that if the tip of the cone points downwards, then a south wind is expected while a northerly wind is indicated by hoisting the point upwards. Another warning sign is a red flag; if this is flown from the same pier, it means there is at least nine feet of water in the harbour entrance, something the larger vessels need to know if they are to cross it.

To the east lies a dangerous sandbank, Smethwick Sands, which is covered by shallow water and which, in gale conditions, causes rough water with a consequent danger to shipping. It is marked at each end by a buoy with a flashing light. Even now, people remind Dolly of a terrible storm and gales in 1871 when the lifeboat was smashed to pieces and most of its crew drowned. Today lifeboats are still a vital part of everyday life in these seaside resorts and their bases are open to the public – she finds their history and the bravery of their volunteer crews quite astonishing.

The fresh water in the harbour comes from the Gipsey Race, a fast-flowing stream which rises on the Yorkshire Wolds thirteen miles away and a fisherman once showed her a curious ebbing-and-flowing fresh water well only four feet from the shoreline. Beside the harbour Dolly found a fine marine museum and aquarium including a huge fish tank, one of the biggest in the country. It is fed by sea water and displays a range of marine life from sea scorpions to conger eels by way of crabs and thornback rays!

In the summer Bridlington is packed with visitors, and so when Dolly comes without young Sam she tries to avoid the crowds by calling in either spring or autumn when the resort is quieter, even if the weather can be uncertain.

In touring the town, though, she has discovered that many famous people have been before her. The ancient priory was visited by King Edward II and King Henry V while one of its priors, John of Bridlington, was canonised by the Pope in 1401. Born at nearby Thwing, John studied at Oxford before joining the priory, eventually becoming its prior in 1362.

One famous visitor to Bridlington who received a rough welcome was Queen Henrietta Maria, the wife of Charles I. Beside the harbour is Queen's

Lifeboats are essential for the safety of sea-faring people. Their highly skilled crews are all volunteers and the lifeboat houses are usually open to the public. Here, Scarborough lifeboat attracts an interested crowd.

House and it was to that house that she fled from a ship while being hunted by the Parliamentarians. Next day the ships bombarded the town hoping to flush her out but Henrietta hid in a ditch. Later she wrote to Charles and said, 'Before I was out of bed, the balls whistled over my head and you can imagine I did not like the music. So, dressed as I could, I went on foot some distance and got shelter in a ditch.'

She added that a sergeant was killed only twenty yards away and that she remained there for two hours, covered with flying earth. On leaving the ditch, she forgot her little dog and had to run back for it, but both lived to tell the tale. And even more bravely, she returned to the house because, as a later report said, she did not want the captains of the Parliamentary ships to have the vanity of saying, 'We made Her Forsake the Towne.'

Bridlington's modern welcome to visitors is much more friendly and Dolly made a mental note to inform Henry Wilks of the nature reserves nearby. There are Bempton Cliffs, the only mainland gannet colony in Britain with spectacular birds like the guillemot, puffins and kittiwakes, and there is also Spurn Point which is owned by the Yorkshire Naturalists Trust. Only yards wide in places, it juts into the sea with a lighthouse and some coastguard cottages near the tip, but this is also a haven of wildlife, especially sea birds and waders. There is limited access to Spurn Point.

In addition, on a recent visit she discovered that Charlotte Brontë had visited Bridlington, the author's first visit to the seaside. It was in 1839 when Charlotte was twenty three, and it was also her first railway trip. Dolly made a firm resolve to tell Rachel Hughes about this, knowing that Rachel was studying Charlotte's novel *Jane Eyre* for her A level exam.

On an earlier occasion, with Sam eager to ride on the clifftop railway known as the Bridlington Belle, Dolly took him to Sewerby Hall which provides fine entertainment and relaxation for all ages. It stands about two miles out of the town and was acquired by Bridlington council in 1934 for the benefit of the town and its people, a far-sighted decision. Today the Hall boasts an intriguing mixture of Regency and Georgian styles, with some of its 1714 decorations still on show. It includes a museum, art gallery, zoo, gardens, golf course, restaurant and the famous Amy Johnson room.

Dolly had always admired Amy Johnson, the pioneer lady aviator from Hull, who opened this hall to the public in 1936. When she died in an aircraft crash in 1941 her father presented her collection of artefacts to Sewerby Hall where it remains a major attraction. On view are items such as her log book, various medals from all over the world and even a silk kimono presented to her in 1931 upon her flight to Tokyo. Seeing all Amy's trophies and mementos of her travels made Dolly wistful; perhaps, one day, she would travel overseas and fly in an aircraft . . .

But if Dolly did not travel to foreign shores, she did return again and again to Bridlington's near neighbour, Scarborough. It is renowned as the Queen of Watering Places and is England's earliest seaside resort. Magnificently positioned on the North Yorkshire coast, it occupies two huge bays separated

Scarborough's beach in the South Bay is always crowded in summer. The area is rich with colourful buildings such as sea-food stalls, bingo halls, amusement arcades and cafés. The beach is sandy and spacious when the tide is out.

by a promontory which is topped by a twelfth-century castle. This most popular of seaside resorts has long been a favourite of Dolly's. She has stayed here with Matt and Sam, renting a second-floor flat overlooking Valley Bridge which gave them easy access to the sands where Sam discovered the donkeys. These patient and loveable animals work so hard to please the children.

Sam loves the foreshore in the South Bay with its brash and gaudy exterior, superficial but colourful frontages and range of whelk stalls, bingo halls, amusement arcades and cafes. He likes the ghost train, the plastic monsters that leer out of shops and the souvenirs that he can buy for a few pennies. He loves Mr Marvel's Leisure and Amusement Park with its dinosaur kingdom and mammoth, as well as a giant roller coaster, the largest in Yorkshire. Matt would never go on that but Dolly did take little Sam who screamed with delight the whole time. As they strolled through the crowds in the South Bay, Sam was excited by the noise and laughter of people enjoying themselves, the clatter of coins dropping into fruit machines, the smell of fish-and-chips and vinegar, the cries of joy coming from children on the swings and roundabouts on the beach, the open-topped bus that cruises to and fro to show passengers the sights. There is the crunch of sand underfoot as it is swept from the edge of the sea to make a fine layer along the surfaces of the roads and pavements, swirling into the shops and cafes. Dolly even found a hospital whose front door opens almost on to the beach. As a tiny boy, Sam had clutched his mother's hand as she had walked him through these magic sights, just as Dolly herself had clutched her mum's many years earlier. There is the harbour, too, a busy place with fishing boats, cargo ships and holiday cruisers all bobbing up and down on the swell of the water.

But it was the North Bay that provided Sam with further delights. There, everything seemed so huge and open. There was the Water Scene with two of the world's biggest water slides. Nearly 200 metres long, some 1,500 gallons of water cascade down each one every minute and people can slide down to plop squealing with delight into the shallow waters of the swimming pool below. Sam did not have a go on his first visit; he felt too frightened but promised his mum that he would slide down it when he was a big boy. He also liked looking at the jacuzzi, the water cannon, and the diving boards with children jumping off to make huge splashes while their mums and dads sunbathed on the nearby roof.

Then Sam had found Kinderland, a tree-lined park full of things to play on without restriction, a playground designed especially for children up to fourteen. One payment allows them to play on everything, all day if they want to. For Sam it was heaven. He soon made friends with another boy of his own age, and as the two amused themselves Dolly had a coffee in the restaurant knowing that Sam would not be in any danger. She wondered how Matt would have liked this place – he might even have had a go on some of the equipment! It looked sturdy enough for dads.

During that visit, Sam had explored the sandpit, roller skated, played crazy golf, slithered down slides, swung on swings, climbed on rope assault courses, nearly got lost in the fantasy maze and dived into the dry swimming pool filled with 50,000 plastic balls. There was boating, a water chute, see-saws and

Scarborough Spa, with the Grand Hotel in the background. In 1698 the Corporation built the first Spaw House where visitors could sample the water and this has grown into the present spa complex (spelt without the w).

aerial thrills ... for young Sam there was so much to do, even more than when he played around the farm.

The following day, Scarborough had produced more surprises when Sam noticed the miniature railway and wanted to ride on it. His insistence persuaded Dolly to explore Northstead Manor Gardens because the tiny railway train chugs through there with its happy passengers via a series of tunnels, bridges and stations. Sam discovered more miniatures, this time battleships and aircraft which stage a realistic and exciting maritime battle on the lake in Peasholm Park. There are four warships and sixteen aircraft which whizz from the trees to repel three enemy invaders, and it is within this stunning park that Dolly found the Open Air Theatre with its boating lake and tree walk which is magical at night when it is illuminated.

In her days at Scarborough, Dolly found Alan Ayckbourn's Theatre in the Round which presents world premières of his plays. She also discovered The Floral Hall with its seasonal entertainments with international stars, the Spa with its own theatre as well as tea dances and musical entertainments, the Valley Gardens and Museum Gardens which together form Scarborough's old park, as well as the curious Rotunda Museum, one of the first ever purpose-built museums. There was the Wood End Museum, too, the former home of the literary Sitwell family, with the Art Gallery next door.

But it was while exploring Scarborough alone that Dolly found the old town. She had never really thought that such a busy, bright and bustling place had any historic aspects other than those which feature so prominently. Yet, just behind the harbour, through an alley that leads into Quay Street, she discovered a fascinating network of ancient streets and houses. The contrast was remarkable for, within a few strides, the scene changed to olde worlde Scarborough with all its individual charms. Quay Street was cobbled with granite lines laid down for the wheels of the old coaches, then a climb through Tuthill and some narrow alleys, with sudden and stunning views of the sea, brought her face to face with the imposing St Mary's Church. Here she found the grave of Anne Brontë, while in the town centre there was a busy market hall. And beyond lay the bustling modern town centre with its department stores, banks and offices.

With or without Sam, Dolly always found Scarborough fascinating, and the more she explored the town the more secrets she discovered. She knows that Scarborough has more to offer than the bright lights and candy floss of its seafront and shoreline.

Sometimes, as she sat on the sands beneath the imposing Spa complex, she thought of Mrs Farrow who came here in 1620. Described as a 'sensible and intelligent lady', she noticed that some stones on the beach were rust coloured where fresh water ran across them. When tasted, that water was more acid than ordinary water and when she persuaded scientists to examine it, they found it contained health-giving minerals. Within a short time 'several persons of great quality travelled many miles to drink it.'

They preferred it to the Italian, German or French spaws. And so Scarborough's early fame as a spa town began. In 1698 the Corporation built the first Spaw House where the visitors could sample the waters and this has grown and changed until it is now the famous Spa, spelt without the w.

Millions of people have come to Scarborough over the last 300 years and millions more will come in the future. And among them will be Dolly Skilbeck.

It was during a stay in Scarborough, with a car at her disposal, that Dolly explored the coastline to the north. She halted a while at Ravenscar with its unrivalled views across Robin Hood's Bay and undertook the breathtaking climb down to the beach. Nearby is Beast Cliff where bygone sailors filled their water casks from a waterfall known as The Watersplash as it tumbled directly over the cliffs into the sea. This tiny, isolated clifftop community was once a Roman fort, then the Danes came in AD 866 to oust them and to hoist their famous flag with its raven image, but even now only a handful of people live there.

Robin Hood's Bay, with its narrow streets and picturesque cottages, is perched on the edge of the North Sea. At times, the tide flows along the main street and the village is named after the legendary hero of Sherwood Forest who is said to have here sheltered from his enemies. (Photograph by J. Allan Cash.)

The clifftop village of Ravenscar offers breathtaking views along the coastline with Robin Hood's Bay in the distance. (Photograph by J. Allan Cash.)

It was the view of Robin Hood's Bay that tempted Dolly to visit the legendary haunt of the famous outlaw. The bay faces almost due east, and after the drive down narrow lanes and incredibly steep hills she halted in the village described by John Leland in 1892 as 'one of the quaintest places imaginable'. He went on to say that it 'hangs in picturesque confusion on the steep sides of a narrow gully; it is yet another of these North Yorkshire fishing villages which clings to the cliffs and whose houses continue to drop into the sea.'

And so they do. The village is perched on the edge of the sea and the older houses crowd the shoreline as narrow passages twist and turn between them. One anonymous lady travel writer said it was the strangest village it had been her fortune to behold. It is, without doubt, one of the most astonishing sights on the Yorkshire coastline for the high tide literally flows up the village street. Some residents told Dolly of a ship's bowsprit smashing the window of a pub and showed her that where cars would normally park at the end of the street, there are fishing boats and nets as the sea splashes across the yellow 'No Parking' lines. After exploring the village, Dolly wandered on to the layers of sea-weed covered rocks which form the beach but became alarmed as the tide swept in and rose at an incredibly fast rate. Taken by surprise, she had to run for the shore with the rising water lapping at her heels. She learned from a cafe owner that holidaymakers often get stranded on those rocks – they are no place for a youngster like Sam.

The enormous charm of Robin Hood's Bay has made it a haven for writers and artists. Leo Walmsley lived here and made his name with a novel called *Three Rivers* in which Robin Hood's Bay was featured as Bramblewick. This was later filmed as 'The Turn of the Tide'.

The village has also had a long and romantic association with smuggling, and even now there are hidden panels in some of the houses with secret cellars and escape routes . . . or so it is said! But the bay's most renowned visitor, and perhaps the first to arrange group holidays here, was Robin Hood. Whenever he was in serious danger, he and his men would flee to Robin Hood's Bay. Robin must have been a good organiser of trips because there were about a hundred of his merrie men! Here they could rest and hide until danger had passed, and if the hunters were getting too close the outlaws would simply take boats to sea until the hunters had gone. A fleet of small boats was on constant standby and when Robin Hood was in the village he called himself Simon Wise. The local people always protected him against pursuers for he helped those in need while staying here. At that time the village had no name and in 1532, many years after his death, it was named in his honour.

Another of Dolly's favourite Yorkshire resorts is Whitby with its ancient abbey of St Hilda superbly positioned on the cliff at the top of 199 ancient steps. Sometimes, with Sam at her side, she has tried to count those steps, and not once has she agreed with the official total . . . but each of her counts has been different.

Once called Streonshalh, the town has been a noted fishing port for centuries but its abbey has made it renowned throughout the Christian world. Originally it was a small wooden building and remained as such throughout the reign of the mighty St Hilda as abbess; a stone replacement only following upon her death in AD 680, but that is not the one seen today. In Hilda's time Streonshalh Abbey became renowned as a centre of religion and learning. It was here, in AD 644, that the Synod of Whitby determined the British method of calculating the date of Easter. And that method is still used. It is also the birthplace of English poetry for it was here that the cowherd Caedmon suddenly found himself able to sing of the creation in beautiful verse. The abbey which stands today is a further replacement but it was surrendered to Henry VIII at the Reformation amid tears from the Whitby people.

In addition to Whitby's renown as a fishing port, it has seen booms in whaling, alum and jet mining, the last reaching its pinnacle during Victorian times. When Queen Victoria wore some hand-carved jet jewellery with its deep black sheen, the fashionable ladies copied her. The boom expired at the turn of the century, but jet is still carved in the town and so, on a recent visit, Dolly sought a shop to buy a jet brooch for Annie. She found a delightful necklace with a cross and bought that.

In seeking the shop, she walked beside the harbour with its foreign and British fishing fleets and its curious swing bridge. There is a new bridge across the River Esk in the upper harbour and it was opened in 1980 to provide staggering views of Whitby but the old one continues in use by the towns-

Whitby is a curious mixture of old and new buildings. Quaint red-roofed cottages line the harbour-side and the famous 199 steps lead to the abbey which is high on the cliff.

In 1536 Whitby was described as a 'great fischer towne', and in addition to its own fishing fleet it still attracts herring boats and trawlers from other ports and other countries. At times the boats are so closely packed in the harbour that it is possible to walk half way across the harbour by using the decks.

people. Captain James Cook sailed from Whitby to discover Australia, and he used the small Whitby-built boats. Their toughness was legendary – Scoresby used them in his whaling expeditions from Whitby to the Arctic, and other noted seamen have sailed from here, including Captain Stephen Wharton who was the first man to carry elephants on board ship!

Dolly found Whitby a fascinating but curious mixture of buildings old and new. Garish modern structures line the lower harbour, such as bingo halls, amusement arcades, sea-food stalls and souvenir shops. This contrasts vividly with the quaint red-roofed cottages hidden behind the modern frontage.

60

Access to them is often only by narrow alleys and steep, twisting flights of steps. Many of these have changed little in two or three centuries although one part of the old town round Haggerlyth and Henrietta Street, at the foot of the 199 steps, has recently been renovated and stretches of road re-cobbled. Dolly loves to stroll around that part of the town with its narrow streets, its old Town Hall standing on stone columns and its ghauts which are narrow alleys that reach to the water's edge.

This is yet a further contrast to the West Cliff with its fine hotels and superb Georgian houses which stand in a majestic curve as they look out to sea above the Spa. Here is fine entertainment, while the Pannett Art Gallery and Museum which is surrounded by charming parkland, offers peace for those who seek it. Before leaving Whitby, Dolly bought a present for Annie, Joe and Kate – some Whitby kippers smoked over oak shavings in the traditional way.

Another call was at Staithes, the most northerly village in Yorkshire and one which also clings to the cliffs in an astonishing manner. It is possible to pass through the village without realising that an entirely different world exists below the rim of the cliffs. At the foot of the steep hill, down which visitors' cars are forbidden, is a conglomeration of tiny stone cottages, steep steps and narrow alleys which are packed so tightly that few of the homes have gardens or room for lawns or extensions. They seem to press together for protection against the sea, and down the years scores of houses have indeed been washed into the waves. The whiff of fish always reminds Dolly that this is a hard-working fishing village which has not been ruined by tourism. There is no room for amusement arcades and bingo halls, but it was to this place that

Whitby's twin piers give protection to the harbour from the turbulent North Sea.

61

Staithes is the most northerly village in Yorkshire and its cottages cling to the cliffs in a most spectacular manner. It remains largely unspoilt by tourism and continues to be a fishing community.
(Photograph by John Bethell.)

young James Cook came around 1740 to be an apprentice to a grocer called Sanderson. He left Staithes to become our most famous seafarer and the discoverer of a new continent.

Dolly loved to see the women in their curious Staithes bonnets and learned that a custom here, among the older folk, is to wear a white sash at funerals.

Quaint, lovely and fascinating in the extreme, she found Staithes a delight and was determined to return. Before driving back to Emmerdale, she climbed along a cliffside footpath and discovered she had ascended Boulby Cliffs which are England's highest, and they overlook Boulby Potash Mine which is Europe's deepest.

5

Seth around the moors

SETH Armstrong is every inch a countryman and would never contemplate spending his leisure time in a town or city. As he says, 'Towns and cities is places to come from, not to go to. I know a lot of folks that come from Sheffield.' Although his work involves the countryside and its wildlife, it is to the countryside that he goes in his leisure moments.

Among his favourite haunts are the North York Moors which contain England's largest expanse of open heather. The majestic landscape, many miles to the east of the Yorkshire Dales, offers solitude of a kind rarely found in modern Britain. Often when walking across these heights, the only sound other than the wind whispering through the heather or a trickling moorland stream is the call of the grouse or the bleating of a moorland sheep. These hardy animals live unfenced upon these moors.

The heather provides a breathtaking blanket of purple in the autumn but becomes dark and brooding during the rigours of winter. This magnificent corner of Yorkshire, covering some 553 square miles, is one of the country's most beautiful national parks and it is rich with pretty villages. Their sturdy residents enjoy a unique way of life in the remote and steep-sided dales.

From the heights of the moors it is possible to enjoy spectacular long-distance views, while down in the dales there is peace and solitude beside rippling streams which flow through shaded woodlands or lush meadows carpeted in colourful displays of wild flowers. It is here that the bees and butterflies work without fear of pollution while the fresh waters of the rivers offer a range of coarse and sporting fishing that appeals to people the world over. The waters of the River Esk, for example, are pure enough to contain the king of sporting fish, the salmon, with trout and grayling being a feature of this and many other pure-watered moorland becks.

There are no towns on the moors, although the region is surrounded by several fascinating market towns like Guisborough, Loftus, Stokesley, Thirsk, Helmsley, Kirkbymoorside, Pickering and Malton, with the resorts of Scarborough and Whitby dominating the dramatic coastline. But on the moors, Seth was pleased to discover, there are country pubs with tasty ales and mouth-watering beers which complement bar snacks and evening meals. Some of

Seth Armstrong.

Malton is one of the market towns which surround the North York Moors. It was an important Roman town called Derventio and is now an interesting place with its large market place and old houses. The town is sometimes called New Malton because the village of Old Malton stands about a mile away. The church at Old Malton was formerly a Gilbertine Priory.

these inns occupy lofty and lonely sites – for example, there is the Lion Inn on Blakey Ridge near the site of an ancient cockpit, and the Saltersgate Inn between Pickering and Whitby where the peat fire has burned for more than a century and a half.

These remote inns are popular with ramblers and hikers who trek across the heights on long-distance paths such as the Cleveland Way, the Crosses Walk or the Lyke Wake Walk. Lower down the dales are other inns favoured by holidaymakers and day-trippers. Short-term visitors come to cottages and caravan sites or visit parts of the moors during a day trip from the larger conurbations of York, Hull, Middlesbrough, Darlington, Stockton, Sunderland and beyond.

The variety of wild creatures to be found on the moors is a naturalist's dream, and attracts ornithologists, students, photographers and artists, all of whom come to savour the sight of so many beautiful creatures in their natural state. There may be a heron standing like a sentinel in the waters of the River Derwent in Forge Valley as it awaits a passing fish, or a fox sidling through the undergrowth of Baxtons Wood near Cowhouse Bank above Helmsley. Weasels and stoats dart across the quiet lanes while gloriously coloured kingfishers swoop along the rivers with their piping calls. The forests contain deer, badgers and jays, while flocks of wintering geese and rarer waterfowl head for the inland waters like Scaling Reservoir or Lockwood Beck. Summer visitors such as the cuckoo, swift and swallow all come to areas of these moors, as do predators like the hen harrier or even the buzzard. There are snakes, too, like the adder, or viper as it is sometimes known, and the harmless grass snake which alarms those who do not recognise it.

And as if that was not enough, the moors contain vivid and nostalgic reminders of a past way of life. These include the country's sole collection of witch posts which were built into cottages to prevent the evil of witches, and there are the steam trains of the North York Moors railway, the quoit games of Beckhole, the largest collection of standing stones and crosses, some 1,300 in all, an annual display of giant gooseberries at Egton Bridge and the power of the courts-leet which still operate on the moors to protect rights of way and common land. And there are village agricultural shows with their delightful contests which range from the Most Tasty Bilberry Pie and the Brownest Half-Dozen Eggs to the Best Dressed Shire Horse.

But even on the moors Seth cannot always avoid work, for his reputation as a connoisseur of beer and associated country matters is such that show committees regularly seek his advice. On many occasions Seth has been asked to be a judge at moorland shows.

'Ah've judged most things,' he laughed. 'Apple pies, carved walking sticks, watercolours of Amos Brearly, poems about poachers, jars o' bramble jam and hand-knitted caps, but it's t'home-made beer that Ah like best. Ah reckon Ah'm a fair judge o' that – Ah give 'em all first prize, tha knaws, after giving 'em a fair long tasting with a few second helpings just to be sure Ah'm reet in me judgement . . .'

It was during one of these judging sessions that Seth befriended a gamekeeper who worked for a large estate, most of whose open land lay upon the moors. His name was Aaron Harland and when Seth explained that he was also a gamekeeper, Aaron offered to show him his beat. Seth readily accepted, feeling sure he would benefit by the traditional gift of a brace of game birds.

Aaron was a man approaching retirement, a dour man born and bred on the North York Moors with a round, ruddy, weather-tanned face and the stamina of a moorland sheep. He explained that the chief difference between his own beat and Seth's was that his comprised acre upon acre of open, heather-clad moorland, whereas Seth's was chiefly woodland and meadow surrounding Alan Turner's fish-farm. The two beats were vastly different, with completely separate problems. Even as gamekeeper for NY Estates, Seth's beat had not included open moorland of the kind cared for by Aaron. Whereas Seth had reared pheasants for shooting in the woodlands and fields as game, Aaron's task was to ensure that the grouse flourished on the remote heights and that the heather was maintained in peak condition.

Aaron began by showing Seth the shooting butts. These were stone-built shelters spaced at intervals across the moors, some of them following the lines of roads or ancient pathways. They were each about the height of a dry-stone wall and formed a hollow square, often with a lining of heather along the top. The guns, as the shooters are known, conceal themselves in the butts as teams of beaters walk in a long line across the moor, driving the grouse towards the guns while compelling them to take flight. The shooting season for grouse begins on the Glorious Twelfth of August and continues until 10 December, with guns competing for the honour of bagging the first brace of the season, or perhaps the largest bag.

'You'll get the anti-shooting protestors, Ah'll bet?' asked Seth.

'Aye,' agreed Aaron, 'But the silly devils don't know owt about game preservation. My bosses and their friends shoot grouse because it ensures the species doesn't die out. I mean, all estates owners want the grouse to survive, don't they? If we stopped shooting them, they'd be extinct within a few years and no landowner wants that to happen. Then we've got to keep the heather in good shape by burning it. If we don't care for t'heather, t'bracken'll take over and if there's no heather, our grouse will die because they feed on it and live in it. No heather, no grouse. And no grouse means no income to pay for the upkeep of the heather. It's all part of one system.'

Seth nodded his understanding, but Aaron went on, 'And if we don't shoot some of the grouse, too many will breed and there'll not be enough shelter or food for them all. They've all got an inherent disease, you see, it attacks and kills all the weak birds so we've got to cull them to keep all the birds strong enough to avoid being weakened by that disease.'

'It's hard to convince townies of that,' smiled Seth, wondering where the nearest pub was. There seemed to be nothing up here but acres of heather, a lot of stone crosses and flocks of black-faced moorland sheep that nobody fences in. They roam the heights with total freedom, although each animal knows its own 'heeaf' or home.

'You could do with a pint?' grinned Aaron, as if reading Seth's mind.

'Ah could that!'

Among the sights of the North York Moors are the steam trains which operate between Grosmont and Pickering. The original line, built on the advice of George Stephenson, was officially opened on 26 May 1836 and contained astonishing feats of engineering. It crossed boggy areas on beds of trees and heather bound in sheepskins and it climbed to over 500 feet (150 metres) by use of a system of balancing weights which incorporated full water tanks. Today the line is a major tourist attraction as well as a service.

SETH AROUND THE MOORS

'I don't drink,' said Aaron. 'But we'll find a pub.'

As they walked towards a moorland pub, they disturbed a pair of grouse. They rose from the heather, clattering from the ground with a whirring of wings as they chattered in their guttural voice. 'Go-back, go-back, go-back.'

Aaron explained that the red grouse lives only in Great Britain, although it has cousins in Europe, Asia and North America. It is about the size of a small domestic hen with rich red-brown plumage and white furry legs. Two distinctive red eye-wattles can be seen if one gets close enough. On the North York Moors, they are known as moor birds, or 'moorbods'. The red grouse is dumpy with short wings, consequently it does not fly very well or very far. When it has to take to the air, it will rise suddenly from the heather with a clatter of its wings and rapidly zig-zag in a short but noisy flight before gliding swiftly to earth to vanish beneath the covering of heather.

There it will run along tunnels among the heather; it makes these by running along regular tracks and in winter will even paddle down the snow so that these tracks are kept clear and the heather remains exposed for its food. In winter, heavy snow settles on top of the heather, thus leaving these tunnels open for the grouse. It will feed on the heather throughout the year, eating different parts of the plant and consuming the seeds in the autumn.

Its rapid weaving and low flight makes it a difficult target and so the bird is an attraction for shooting parties. The income from these parties allows the landowners to maintain the heather moors, which are very costly to upkeep. One vital part of the upkeep is heather burning. Between 1 November and 31 March the landowners burn the heather, destroying all the tough old shoots of expired plants so that the new growth can establish itself to provide food and shelter for the grouse. This must be done in the winter months because in summer the peat base upon which the heather grows might catch fire. This thick and spongy layer provides nourishment for all the moors, and if it is destroyed it will herald the disappearance of all moorland life – birds, insects, plants, reptiles and animals. The controlled burning of areas of moorland operates on a six-year rota, the burned portions being called swizzens or swiddens. Without this care, even the domestic sheep could not live on the moors and many smallholdings would be at risk, with a huge loss of jobs.

'So you see,' said Aaron, 'heather and grouse are therefore vital to one another and vital to man.'

'A bit like a good pint,' beamed Seth as they reached the inn where he allowed Aaron to buy him a pint, just so as Aaron, a non-drinker, knew what it was like to buy a pint for a pal. Afterwards, Seth was duly presented with a brace of grouse before he went home. He decided he wanted to find out more about the North York Moors and their inns.

It was upon a later visit that Aaron showed him a selection of the moorland crosses. They had met in Rosedale where Seth had left his car and they had climbed to the heights in Aaron's official vehicle, a Range Rover.

The North York Moors contain the country's largest assembly of standing stones, certainly the largest in such a compact area, and they include parish

boundary markers, the remains of stone circles, earthworks, way marks, religious crosses and memorials of various kinds. Some of them honour significant events, such as the remarkable discoveries of Captain James Cook, himself a lad from the moors. Another stone, the ancient Lilla Cross, dates from AD 626 and is a memorial to a Christian called Lilla. He saved the life of King Edwin of Northumbria by stepping into the path of a poisoned sword wielded by an assassin. Lilla died instead of the king and Edwin was so impressed by this selfless devotion that he became a Christian and was eventually baptised by St Paulinus.

The three white radomes of Fylingdales Ballistic Missile Early Warning Station on the moors above Goathland sit like massive golf balls among an expanse of heather. Some thirty years old, they are to be replaced in 1992 by a new flat-topped pyramid-style structure.

Later he built a church which we now call York Minster. Lilla Cross stands literally in the shadows of Fylingdales Ballistic Missile Early Warning Station on Fylingdales Moor and it is therefore one of the nation's earliest Christian relics and a reminder of that ancient murder.

Aaron took Seth to one of the viewpoints on the moors when one can turn almost in a full circle to enjoy a vast panorama on all sides. It is the meeting place of roads from Rosedale, Castleton, Westerdale and Hutton-le-Hole, and standing at this point is Young Ralph, more widely, but erroneously, known as Ralph's Cross. Nine feet high on its pillar of local stone, this beautiful cross forms the logo of the North York Moors National Park and has a tiny hollow in the top.

In bygone times, travellers would place coins there for the benefit of those less fortunate, but the cross has been damaged by modern people attempting to find money. Having received a leg-up from Aaron, Seth popped a handful of loose coins into the hollow, just to maintain the custom. Within sight of Young Ralph are Old Ralph, Fat Betty and the Margery Stone. This family of stones is said to commemorate the occasion when Sister Elizabeth from Baysdale Abbey arranged to meet Sister Margery from Rosedale Abbey at this point. A thick fog descended and the nuns got lost, only being traced through the good sense of a guide called Ralph.

OPPOSITE *For such a compact area, the North York Moors contain what is probably the country's largest collection of standing stones, some 1,300 in total. They include crosses, boundary markets, memorials, way marks, earthworks and stone circles.*

69

But from this elevated point, Seth could see an astonishing array of deep dales and lofty ridges. Aaron showed him Ryedale, Westerdale, Farndale and Rosedale, but Seth expressed interest in the one that lay to the north in a vast cleft in the moors. This is Eskdale, the largest of the dales within the North York Moors and one which differs from the others in that it lies from west to east. Most of the others open to the south. The River Esk, after which the dale is named, enters the North Sea at Whitby and attracts many tributaries, and, as Seth had already been told, it is a first-rate salmon river. Seth reckoned that if it attracted fishermen of the quality who'd legally fish for salmon then there'd be a few good pubs beside the river.

But there is more than fish in this dale. Eskdale is the home of the Cleveland Bay horse, originally the Chapman Horse. A chapman was a tinker and such characters made use of these tough animals to carry pots and pans from village to village. Broad backed and sure footed, they were also used for ploughing, hunting, and even hauling coaches. When better roads allowed coaches to be drawn more speedily, the Chapman was crossed with the best racing horses of the day to produce the famous Cleveland Bay. This is the most beautiful breed of coaching horse the world has ever seen and it continues to be bred on the moors. On ceremonial and state occasions, Cleveland Bays draw the Queen's coach, and in 1984 she gave a reception at Windsor Castle in honour of the Cleveland Bay.

'That'll be t'horse we see on Bay Horse pub signs?' grinned Seth, thinking it was time to explore that possibility.

'Aye,' agreed Aaron, 'except the artists usually get it wrong. The Cleveland Bay has a long black tail and mane, but most of them show it with a short tail.'

Aaron explained that in the dale spread before them Danby still boasts a Court Leet and Baron which administers common law and rights of way, while Danby Castle is occupied as a working farmhouse; once it was home to Catherine Parr, sixth wife of Henry VIII. Below it is Duck's Bridge, built in 1386, a packhorse bridge which is more ancient than Beggar's Bridge further downriver at Glaisdale.

Seth asked to be shown more of Eskdale and so Aaron began by dropping into Danby Dale for a tour of Botton Village. Since 1965 this has housed a community of mentally and physically handicapped people who maintain themselves by making and selling goods from their own shops. The village is one of several established by the Camphill Village Trust, both in the UK and overseas.

They passed through Castleton where a pub sign invited Seth in by saying:

> Kind gentlemen and yeoman good,
> Call in and drink with Robin Hood;
> If Robin Hood be not at home
> Step in and drink with Little John.

Farndale is one of the more remote and rugged dales of the moors but around Easter it is a picture when millions of wild daffodils bloom beside the gentle River Dove.

'I think I'll just pop in to see Little John,' grinned Seth.
'You won't,' said Aaron. 'It's shut and he's out.'

They drove through Lealholm which boasts England's largest rock garden in a wild chasm known as Crunkley Gill where the shaded Esk cascades over rugged rocks. But this is private property and not open to the public. The top of Lealholm Bank has some stupendous views. One foreign travel writer said, 'They differ from all others I have ever seen, and in this particular – that elsewhere you have to go in search of beautiful views; here, they come and offer themselves to be looked at.'

In Glaisdale Seth spotted a pub called the Angler's Rest and felt that as he worked on Alan Turner's fish farm it was very apt that he should pop in for some refreshment, but Aaron said there was no time. In Glaisdale the two gamekeepers halted at Beggar's Bridge where Aaron explained the story of its construction. He showed Seth a stone on the parapet bearing the initials TF and the date 1619, then explained that in the sixteenth century a man called Tom Ferris fell in love with Agnes Richardson of Glaisdale. But Tom, who worked on board ship under Sir Francis Drake as a lowly deckhand, spent his holidays with relations at Egton. He was very poor and Agnes' father, the local squire, objected to the relationship. The devoted Tom persisted, however, and he had to wade across the River Esk to meet Agnes. They met in secret, with Agnes placing a light in her window when it was safe to call. But Squire Richardson was equally persistent and said Tom could never marry Agnes. Then one day Tom plucked up his courage and asked, 'Sire, if I make my fortune and become as wealthy as you, will you then allow me to marry Agnes?'

The squire had laughed at this but said he would agree – if Agnes would wait that long. Tom wanted to tell Agnes about this promise and to tell her

Ryedale, on the southern edge of the moors, contains a host of pretty villages. One of them is Hovingham, the childhood home of HRH The Duchess of Kent where the village cricket pitch is upon the lawns of her family house at Hovingham Hall.

he would make his fortune. But before he could do so, he was recalled to his ship. The date was 7 May 1588. An urgent message said he must rejoin Sir Francis Drake who was gathering ships to fight for Queen Elizabeth and England against the Spanish. Tom barely had time to tell Agnes that he would be away for a long time and ran all the way with his news. From the top of Limber Hill he saw a light burning in her window – but the River Esk was in flood and he could not cross it. There was no way he could inform Agnes of his decision and he had to leave without seeing her.

He fought alongside Drake against the Spanish Armada and distinguished himself, with a personal commendation from Drake who afterwards invited Tom to join him on other expeditions. They sailed the seas with Tom eventually becoming a pirate. He seized many rich foreign vessels and in 1592, still only twenty-four, he returned to London with a captured foreign ship. He sold it and became a rich man. His first task was to claim the hand of the girl he had left behind so suddenly; he was now a man of wealth and culture and the Squire, a man of his word, agreed. And throughout those long years, faithful Agnes had waited.

Tom established a highly successful shipping business in Hull and in 1614, aged forty-six, he became Sheriff of Hull. But in 1618 Agnes died and the distraught Tom absorbed himself in civic duties, eventually becoming Lord Mayor of Hull. And then in 1619 he decided to build a bridge at Glaisdale and dedicate it to his Agnes. That graceful bridge remains today so that future lovers might cross the Esk in safety.

'That's a grand tale,' Seth conceded. 'But I bet he wouldn't have built yon bridge if he'd courted my Meg!'

They passed into the tiny Egton Bridge, the village missed by the Reformation. The bravery and dedication of the village's noted martyr, Father Nicholas Postgate, is honoured in the huge Roman Catholic church. Egton Bridge is also noted for its annual show of giant gooseberries, held on the first Tuesday in August.

In Grosmont they saw some engines and coaches of the North York Moors Steam Railway and went on to Beckhole, famed for its quoit matches and its local inn.

'Now, Ah've read about this pub,' said Seth. 'Its sign is an original oil painting, done by Algernon Newton, RA, the father of Robert Newton who became famous for his portrayal of Long John Silver in *Treasure Island*. See, Ah do know summat!'

'And that's earned you a pint,' grinned Aaron. But they were too late. The pub was shut for the afternoon.

In Goathland, Aaron persuaded Seth to make the trek down to Mallyan Spout, one of several beautiful local waterfalls known as fosses. Goathland is a fine centre for exploration of the moors with moorland sheep keeping the greens neatly trimmed while a troop of Plough Stots provide regular entertainment in a type of sword dance.

Aaron drove towards Pickering, showing Seth the impressive Fylingdales

73

*Helmsley is a beautiful
market town on the southern
edge of the North York
Moors. With superb shops, a
fine market square, a castle
and a stately home boasting
links with Bonny Bobby
Shaftoe, it attracts visitors
from a wide area. It is the
location of the offices of the
North York Moors National
Park authority.*

Early Warning Station on its lonely site high on the moors, and the equally
lonely Saltersgate Inn, once a busy coaching inn and now rich with legends.
The peat fire has never been out for some 150 years and an exciseman of old,
murdered by smugglers, lies buried beneath the hearth.

'Ah reckon Ah'll not have a pint there!' decided Seth.

There was no time to walk along Wade's Causeway, a Roman road
stretching for over a mile on the heights, and instead the pair of gamekeepers
ascended to the rim of the Hole of Horcum, a giant depression said to have
been hollowed out by the devil. Moments later they dropped into Dalby
Forest where there is a Forestry Information Centre and a network of forest
trails rich in wild life. The trails lead through the forest to Hackness near
Scarborough, the site of a monastery built as long ago as AD 680. It was at
nearby Brompton Dale that the world's first manned flight in an aircraft took
place; Sir George Cayley's coachman was offered the honour of being pilot
but gave in his notice. He said he was hired to drive, not to fly. This was fifty-
one years before the Wright Brothers flew their famous machine.

Once out of the dense pine forests, they pressed on through Thornton-le-
Dale which once earned the title of Yorkshire's prettiest village – even if it
does have a main road running through the centre. It also boasts England's
most photographed thatched cottage in a picturesque setting beside the stream.
Pickering was next with its ancient castle and steam railway terminus but there
was no time to halt because Aaron had to get back across the moors to see to

his stock. He took Seth via Cawthorne with its four Roman camps and spectacular views, and from there they wound their way into Cropton, once the home of a witch called Awd Mother Migg and now the location of a pub that makes its own beer.

'No time for drinking now,' said Aaron. 'Besides, it's still closing time.'

He hurried Seth through Lastingham and into Rosedale with its notoriously steep Chimney Bank (1-in-3 – 33%) before dropping him in the car park. In saying his farewell and thanks, Seth did pass comment that he had an overpowering thirst so Aaron suggested he look out for White Horse at Kilburn. Seth drove via Hutton-le-Hole with its Folk Museum, then Kirkbymoorside and Helmsley, pausing *en route* in Kirkdale to see the cave where animal remains dating from 70,000 years ago were found – but there is no pub in Kirkdale. Helmsley market place was full of cars, but Seth did have time

The Kilburn White Horse. Almost 100 metres long by some 70 metres high, it overlooks the village of Kilburn near Thirsk. Carved in 1857 by the village headmaster and thirty-three local men and children, it is now a landmark which is visible for over seventy miles. A flight of steps gives access to the horse but care must be taken not to damage its outline.

to ask directions to Kilburn. When he arrived, he was horrified to learn that it wasn't a pub – it is a giant chalk carving of a horse!

Over a hundred yards long by seventy-five yards high, it was carved on the hillside by the village schoolmaster and his pupils. It was completed in November 1857 and is the only one of its kind in the north of England. Seth wondered who groomed it. In Kilburn, Seth found the workshops of Robert 'Mousey' Thompson the woodcarver whose symbol of a little mouse carved on all his woodwork can now be found all over the world.

From there, Seth's old car groaned up the 1-in-3 incline of White Horse Bank and he forgot all about his thirst when he saw the view from Sutton Bank Top. Gliders from the Yorkshire Gliding Club were soaring in the skies as the waters of Lake Gormire shimmered below. The view from here embraces a massive slice of Yorkshire including the Yorkshire Dales, the Plain of York and the foothills of the Pennines. Wordsworth had admired the view and so had John Wesley, and now it was the turn of Seth Armstrong.

As he gazed upon the extensive vista, he knew that deep in those hills lay Beckindale and the Woolpack Inn, only an hour's drive away through Harrogate. He arrived with his moustache twitching at the joyous thought of a pint or two and pushed his way into the bar.

'Pint please, Amos,' he shouted across the room.

'Sorry, Seth, we've had a bus trip in from t'North York Moors. They've supped me clean dry.'

6

Turner on the river bank

Although Alan Turner now spends most of his working days surrounded by carefully tended living fish in tanks and ponds, and at his game farm too, breeding birds for the shoot, his leisure periods are divided between exploration of the river banks and the pursuit of fish. He likes nothing better than to sally forth to the rivers of Yorkshire, there to spend his time either angling or merely walking their banks with the splendour of nature all around him.

In his heart, he admits he is not a born countryman – his deliberately cultivated image is something he has tried hard to achieve because he likes to mingle with, and be accepted by, what he calls the 'right people'. He loves to impress, he loves to live the life of a country gentleman with its hunting, shooting, fishing, good food and fine wines. In this he is not always successful but, in his determination to be accepted, he has spent some years learning to be a competent angler.

He has practised the art of casting, of fly-fishing, of catching the exotic salmon or the succulent trout, of reading the water and of understanding the instincts of those simple but elusive creatures that always seem to outwit him. In his heart of hearts, Alan accepts the wisdom of that great angler, Izaak Walton (1593–1683), who said, 'No man is born an angler.' He continues to try hard as he learns by watching others and, more often, by his own mistakes.

Alan Turner accepts that successful angling requires a long apprenticeship if one is to become even reasonably competent. But he refuses to be taught by others – his self-esteem will not allow anyone, particularly Seth Armstrong, to know that he requires tuition. So off he goes alone, sometimes with a text book and sometimes with the simple aim of spending a whole day learning how to cast his line accurately into a distant pool. He will spend hours beside a river, casting his line again and again until he feels he has achieved some degree of success. He will sit alone, tying flies, testing floats, correcting his casting technique and aim, sampling differing kinds of bait and attempting to understand the natural instincts of freshwater fish. Unfortunately, most of them seem more cunning than Alan Turner and he seldom catches anything. But he does enjoy the outdoor life.

Alan Turner.

For that reason, should anyone take a walk along the banks of any Yorkshire river, expecially during the fishing season, they might find Alan Turner deep in thought and oblivious to everything as he diligently practises with rod and line.

In Yorkshire he is very fortunate because the county boasts thousands of miles of rivers, streams and canals plus a wide selection of inland waters ranging from natural lakes to man-made reservoirs. There is also the rugged and fascinating coastline which, with North Yorkshire and East Yorkshire together, totals more than 117 miles. This presents opportunities for sea-fishing from either boats or piers. In short, there are plenty of places where Alan Turner can spend a quiet time in his desire to become a proficient angler.

No other county has such a choice of rivers. Yorkshire boasts almost 3,600 miles of river (7,200 miles of river bank), and although heavy industry has caused some waters to become too polluted for fish to survive, there remains a large choice of angling venues. The range of available fish varies from salmon, trout and grayling to the coarse fish like chub, dace, barbel, perch, bream and roach, with even the pike and eel offering their own particular challenges.

All the water in those rivers belongs to someone and so permission to fish must be obtained. But fishing is not allowed on all the rivers, and in some cases there is private water which is owned either by estates, companies, individuals or angling clubs. And, as all anglers must be aware, a rod licence is required by anyone over ten years of age. This can be obtained from Yorkshire Water through its various agencies around the county, such as post offices and shops. The income thus generated is used for maintenance and improvement of Yorkshire water.

The longest Yorkshire river is the Swale which is around eighty-three miles in length and is also the fastest flowing of Yorkshire's rivers. The Ure, Wharfe, Aire, Calder and Nidd are all more than fifty miles long, with the Don and

Derwent only a fraction shorter. The shortest is the Bain which is just over two miles long; this pretty river flows from one of Yorkshire's lakes, Semerwater, and later joins the Ure. In addition to these rivers, there are lesser ones and many streams known variously as becks or gills, most offering some scope for angling. The river which contains the greatest flow of water is the Ouse at its confluence with the Humber. Before reaching this point, most of Yorkshire's major rivers flow into it – the Derwent, Swale, Ure, Nidd, Wharfe, Aire, Calder, Dearne and Don all join the Ouse before it broadens to become the Humber. Even the River Trent from Nottinghamshire drains into the Humber by flowing north.

The Yorkshire Esk remains aloof from the drift towards the Ouse for it flows east in its own spectacular valley to join the North Sea at Whitby. This is Yorkshire's only salmon fishing river, although some minor becks do also flow into the sea along the coast. Other than the Esk, therefore, all Yorkshire's major rivers drain the moorlands, dales and plains into the Ouse and Humber, with the unspoilt, pretty Derwent boasting the largest draining area of 775 square miles.

Yorkshire also boasts over 110 reservoirs. Several of the smaller ones are less than 10 acres in area, while some larger ones exceed 100 acres. Gouthwaite Reservoir near Pateley Bridge boasts an acreage of more than 330 acres. The highest earth-filled dam in Great Britain is Scammonden on the Yorkshire Pennines, which is unique because it is crossed by a motorway, the M62. Angling is permitted on over thirty of these reservoirs, with other water sports like sailing, canoeing, rowing, sail boarding and sub aqua being allowed. Facilities for picnic sites, nature studies, bird watching and hiking are also provided around many reservoirs.

And there are the lakes like Semerwater, Gormire, Scarborough Mere and Hornsea Mere (the last being the largest in Yorkshire at 467 acres) and many others, plus miles of placid, unhurried canals in peaceful countryside . . .

The rivers of Yorkshire offer a tempting range of fish – here is a fine catch of trout.

Many Yorkshire rivers begin as fast-moving streams on the fells and moors. The pure water offers a safe haven for fish and other aquatic life.

In his explorations of Yorkshire rivers, however, Alan Turner has been pleasantly surprised by the variety of sights near their banks. In his rather pompous voice, he refers to them as 'riverside furniture' just as his name of 'roadside furniture' includes road signs, pedestrian crossings, traffic lights and bollards. Among his so-called riverside furnishings he has recorded footpaths, wooden bridges, stepping stones, dams, piers, stiles, waterfalls, waths, fords, mills and pumping stations. There are mines and churches, toll roads and castles, as well as some bulls to avoid and battlegrounds to explore.

In some cases there are approved footpaths beside the rivers or around the lakes and reservoirs, although Alan has found that many of these provide rough going, so stout boots and walking sticks are advisable. Trees or shrubs are often conveniently placed to provide useful handholds, and in some areas the paths are wet enough to make wellington boots a necessity. Some stiles can be traps for the unwary because their steps are slippery while some footbridges he has encountered are reminiscent of those flimsy structures which cross bottomless chasms in wildest north America! They sway as one walks across . . . but in truth, those in Yorkshire are only a few feet above the river level and are usually completely safe.

Among the places of interest along the rivers are those which have, over the years, made use of the rivers' abundant water supply. These establishments, which range from sewage works to domestic water supplies, include several mills. For Alan Turner such places were of interest because his own business makes use of water abstracted from Nun's Beck, the stream which flows through Beckindale. Having obtained permission from the Yorkshire Water authority to draw supplies from the beck, Turner's fish farm soon became a flourishing enterprise and he is always keen to discover other businesses which make use of natural water.

One claim is that the first known water mill was established beside a Yorkshire river in 1265; this was the Wharfe at Kettlewell. But Alan discovered a flour mill beside the Esk at Ruswarp, now dismantled to follow the fate of many earlier mills. Several used to operate along that river and in some cases the old mill wheels remain. One is hidden deep in a wood at Glaisdale, for example, and there is another at Danby. Others in the Moors include one at Bilsdale on the River Seph while another near Gayle in Wensleydale dates from 1784 and remains virtually unaltered – its fully operational water turbine is probably the oldest in Britain or possibly in the world. This mill produced cotton and the famous turbine ran for ninety-six years without needing a repair; in recent years it produced electricity for some dales villages. Another restored mill at Newsham near Richmond was used to grind flour during the nineteenth century and is a rare example of its kind. The Yore Mill at Aysgarth is now a coach and carriage museum, and in South Yorkshire there are two mills in industrial museums at Worsborough and Abbeydale, near Sheffield. Turner found less than a dozen in operation throughout Yorkshire, but was delighted with Thwaite Mills which are on an island between the River Aire and the Calder Canal at Stourton, near Leeds. Dating from the 1640s, this complex was used as a fulling mill; this is a process whereby wool is cleaned and given 'body' for later pounding. The mill has also been used for grinding flints and china stone for a local pottery industry and after being Britain's only water-powered stone crushing mill, it is now a museum.

Lower Laithe Reservoir, near Haworth, extends to just over thirty acres. Many offer facilities ranging from water activities like sailing and canoeing to angling and nature study.

Another of Alan's discoveries is Crakehall Water Mill in Wensleydale which makes use of water from Crakehall Beck to produce stoneground wholemeal flour as it did in the time of George I. This mill occupies a site mentioned in the Domesday Survey of 1086 and it was restored as recently as 1980.

Stepping stones are an ancient but popular means of crossing rivers, especially in the higher reaches of the Dales.

Raindale Mill near Pickering is still functioning, too, and produces excellent ground flour, but it no longer occupies its historic site for it has been removed stone by stone to stand behind York's Castle Museum where visitors can buy the freshly ground flour.

One early discovery of Alan Turner's was a derelict waterwheel at Clifford near Boston Spa which was once used to power a flax mill, and another of his favourites is the massive waterwheel at the Water Mill Inn at Foster Beck near Pateley Bridge. At thirty-six feet in diameter, it is thought to be the largest in mainland Britain. To contemplate this huge wheel while he sips a whisky and soda in the Dales sunshine is Alan Turner's idea of bliss.

Five Rise Locks on the Leeds–Liverpool Canal near Bingley are one of the wonders of British engineering. Brought into use in 1774, the five locks make it possible for barges to ascend sixty feet (18.28 metres) in their journey across the Pennines. This is the highest rise along the entire 190 miles of the canal. Nearby, a three-rise lock, a two-rise lock and a single-rise lock allow the canal to rise a total of 120 feet (16.57 metres).

But it was often the unusual items of Turner's 'riverside furniture' that appealed to him. While fishing for trout in Ramsden Reservoir near Holmfirth, for example, he found a wooden bridge over Netherby Clough Beck. On the route of a hilly but pleasing circular walk of about two miles, the bridge is interesting simply because it was built by Boy Scouts! Now it serves those who walk this route which begins between Ramsden Reservoir and Brownhill Reservoir, each known for their game fishing. Game fish is a term which includes brown trout, rainbow trout, salmon trout and salmon. This simple structure and the stone-built Clapper Bridge of Colden near Hebden Bridge are in direct contrast to the famous Five Rise Locks on the River Aire near Bingley. Regarded as one of the wonders of British engineering, the Five Rise Locks are on the Leeds and Liverpool Canal and, together with the Three Rise Locks, provide a pleasant family walk on Sunday

afternoons. As Turner likes to inform those less knowledgeable than himself, a lock is a watertight chamber on a length of canal and it links two lengths of differing heights. This, he says with a chuckle, is how canal water manages to climb hills and so enable barges and boats to cross high ground like the Pennines. It is an astonishing sight to watch barges climb the sixty feet or so by the operation of this series of locks. 'A remarkable piece of river furniture,' says Turner.

There is an intricate network of canals in Yorkshire, many of them in use both commercially and for leisure purposes, while some have recently been renovated and put back into use. But the Leeds–Liverpool is the only one which now crosses the Pennines and is one of the most spectacular. Approved by an Act of Parliament passed in 1770, it took a further forty-six years before it was totally open to traffic, although the section between Bingley and Skipton was in use as early as 1773. One of the difficulties was how to overcome the steep gradients over which the canal was expected to climb, and this is why a series of locks was constructed. That system remains today, a tribute to those early engineers, and it still permits canal vessels to climb the steep slopes of the Pennines.

A report in the *Leeds Intelligencer* of March 1774 said: 'From Bingley to about three miles downwards, the noblest works of the kind that perhaps are to be found in the same extent in the universe are exhibited, viz: a five-fold, a three-fold, a two-fold and a single lock, making together a fall of 120 feet.'

Another feat of canal engineering on the Leeds–Liverpool is an aqueduct known as Priestholme's Changeline Bridge near Gargrave, for this carries the canal over the River Aire. Nearby is what is claimed to be the most spectacular

BELOW RIGHT Even when bordered by mills and industrial buildings, the canals are serene and beautiful. This scene is at Hebden Bridge.

BELOW LEFT Yorkshire's network of canals is used for both commercial and leisure purposes. The Leeds–Liverpool Canal is the only one which now crosses the Pennines and is one of the most spectacular.

length of the entire canal, the stretch between Skipton and East Marton. For Alan Turner the towpath offers solitude and scenery of a kind that he finds most welcome.

But if the towpaths offer peace and solitude of the kind Turner desires, then so do the river banks. Across Yorkshire he has found beautiful abbeys, churches and chapels beside rivers and streams. He has mentioned these to Annie Sugden, knowing of her love of such places, and when he comes upon a place of worship beside a river, he always takes time away from his angling to explore the hallowed walls. High upon his list of interesting places is the tiny parish church of All Saints at Hawnby, near Helmsley in the North York Moors. There was a church here in the twelfth century and the present one stands among a tumble of tombstones amid a mass of snowdrops beside the beautiful River Rye. Here is some interesting Norman stonework, some exquisite stained glass and an ancient stone cross near the font. Not far away at Howsham, near a delightful wooded stretch of the River Derwent, is a lovely chapel of ease built about 125 years ago. With an apsidal chancel, it is light and airy with a belfry and a spire to complete the picture. It was from this tiny village, Turner noted, that a famous Yorkshire entrepreneur came: he was George Hudson, a man who made a fortune out of railways and who became known universally as The Railway King. Alan Turner has often wondered if he will make a fortune out of breeding fish and, if so, how will posterity remember him? Hadn't someone once sneakingly referred to him as the Carping King? It was probably Seth.

One of the most awesome becks, in Turner's opinion, is the Cock Beck which flows beneath the A1 not far from Tadcaster. Little known from both an angling and leisure aspect, its watershed is in the hills to the north of Leeds. From there it meanders east to flow beneath the A1 near Aberford before heading close to Lead church and then north past Towton before entering the River Wharfe near Boston Spa. According to legend, this beck once ran red with blood for three whole days because it was upon its banks, on Palm Sunday in 1461, that the Battle of Towton was fought between the Yorkists and the Lancastrians. This was one of the infamous Battles of the Roses; the Yorkists wearing their emblem of the white rose while the Lancastrians wore the red rose. The Battle of Towton earned the reputation of the bloodiest battle ever fought on English soil, for the death toll was 36,776 men. The ferocious battle between 120,000 soldiers lasted for ten hours during a raging snow storm. Before the two sides engaged in battle, the falling snow created a frightening silence upon the battle field, so much so that the bells of Saxton church could be heard in the distance. As the two armies came face to face, the heavy snow blinded the Lancastrians who were facing into the wind and so the Yorkshire archers snatched up wasted arrows fired by the enemy, for they had fallen too short to be of any danger. With deadly aim, the Yorkists returned them from their own bows and many thousands of the enemy were killed.

The arrival of the Duke of Norfolk with reinforcements for the Yorkists terrified the Lancastrians who fled down the hill towards Towton. But near the Cock Beck, huge numbers were slaughtered before reaching safety. So ended the House of Lancaster, and as their blood flowed into Cock Beck the red coloured water flowed downstream until it joined the River Wharfe which, in turn, became a river of red and so it continued until it flowed into the Ouse, turning this mighty waterway red with the blood of thousands. Some perished in the deep waters of Cock Beck, for the river was in flood and too deep to ford – one of the Lancastrian side who died was Henry Percy, and of him William Shakespeare wrote, 'No braver man ever spurred a courser to the trumpet's sound.'

It is said that the dog roses which grow around the beck and on the former battlefield are flecked with red because they grow from blood-soaked earth. Many of the dead were buried at the tiny church of nearby Lead. This dates to the fourteenth century and is a plain and rather simple building surrounded by meadow land. There are some rough old benches here, with coffin lids dating to the thirteenth century and an ancient font. While the battle raged at Towton, the villagers of tiny Lead were locked in this church to pray for a Yorkist victory. Even today, more than five centuries after that terrible battle, Alan finds the river banks exert an awesome feeling of mystery, terror and dread.

Alan has similar feelings about the mighty, fast-flowing River Swale. For centuries this has been regarded as a holy river, just as other Yorkshire rivers have their own characteristics or share of mystique. The Wharfe, for example, has a reputation for rising and falling very quickly after rain, while years ago the Ure was said to be the haunt of a kelpie who appeared during the evening at Middleham. This carried off those who were unwary of its presence and it was undoubtedly used as a threat to children who might be careless when playing near the water's edge. On the River Tees, which is shared between Yorkshire, Durham and Cleveland, there was a similar spirit called Jenny Greenteeth who trapped the careless into death by drowning, while the Ribble, shared between Yorkshire and Lancashire, had Peg O'Neill. She was a maid at Waddow Hall during the Middle Ages and was drowned, some said by witchcraft practised by her mistress. Ever since, she has claimed a human life once every seven years – this could be avoided by an animal sacrifice such as a cat, dog, cow, sheep or pig.

The Swale also had its spirit; this was the ghost of Tom Hoggart who was a highwayman and he was present in Hoggart's Hole. During the latter years of the eighteenth century, Tom drowned while fleeing from his captors and it is said that his spirit now lurks in the pool which bears his name, there to drown anyone who falls in, no matter how powerful a swimmer the victim may be. But this does not make the Swale a holy river. That claim arises because its pure, fast-flowing waters were used for baptising Christians in much the same way as John the Baptist used the Jordan.

In the case of the Swale, the baptist was Saint Paulinus who was described as 'a tall, stooping form with slender aquiline nose and black hair falling around

86

The weir on the delightful River Wharfe at Linton-in-Craven. The river has a reputation of rising and falling very rapidly after rain.

a thin, worn face. He was of venerable and awe-inspiring appearance.' Paulinus was long remembered in the north because he was appointed Archbishop of York by Pope Honorius I and he later baptised many thousands of converts in the Swale. The location of his holy work is in frequent dispute, but one claim is that he baptised near Aldborough, a village only two miles from Boroughbridge. This was the Roman town of Isurium which now survives as a tourist attraction, but the work of Paulinus occurred a mile or so to the east where the swift Swale joins the gently flowing River Ure after its journey down Wensleydale. Paulinus was a missionary bishop who had been sent to England in AD 601 by Pope Gregory I. When Princess Ethelburga of Kent travelled north to marry Edwin of Northumbria, Paulinus was her chaplain. It was Paulinus who baptised Edwin into the Christian church just as he baptised many thousands of Yorkshire people, and his influence lives on in Yorkshire and elsewhere. It was his work and the baptism of massive crowds of people in the Swale that gave it the reputation of a holy river.

The Ure, on the other hand, is noted for its waterfalls, for as it courses the length of the magnificent Wensleydale it provides numerous falls or fosses as they are known. One of the first is Hardraw Force or foss, the highest single-drop waterfall in England. This was visited by Wordsworth one winter who said that 'on the summit of the cave were three festoons, or rather wrinkles, in the rock, each hung with icicles of various lengths,' while further down stream, and in the river's tributaries, are other waterfalls of less majesty but of equal interest.

For Alan Turner, Aysgarth Falls are supreme for he loves the woodlands and sometimes comes across Henry Wilks here observing wild birds. Turner loves Nidderdale, too, with its towns of Harrogate and Knaresborough both

Yorkshire's waterfalls are spectacular when frozen.

being so rich with attractions. It was in Nidderdale that an obsolete sport was practised. This was wild boar hunting, the dale being one of the last of England's haunts for this persecuted creature.

Alan, when seeking venues to fish and to dine, sometimes climbs to Brimham Rocks where he wanders among these gigantic, wild-sculpted stones to admire the views and enjoy the moorland breezes. There is a massive rock balanced as if upon a pivot; known as the Rocking Stone, it is claimed that it can be moved by the power of one man – but only if that man is totally honest! It is said that few can manage this feat! Another is Lovers Rock from which a young couple leapt intending to kill themselves because their parents objected to their romance. But it is said a good fairy carried them safely to the ground, and when the girl's father witnessed this apparent miracle he consented to a wedding. A guide once showed this stone to Alan Turner with all the serious-ness of his profession and he also showed Alan the Wishing Stone, into which one can poke one's finger while making a wish. Alan refrained from that as he went on to examine the other rocks which bore the grotesque features of beasts both real and mythical.

It is upon heights such as Brimham Rocks that Alan Turner finds happiness. He loves to feel the turf beneath his feet and the wind in his hair as he gazes across the rivers and fells of Yorkshire. And high in those fells are more than a hundred reservoirs, mostly man-made but very pleasant and attractive for all that; there are lakes too, all products of nature at her best. One of them is high in Wensleydale, for here lies the serene beauty of Lake Semerwater which extends for more than 100 acres. It accepts the waters of streams from three dales: Bardale, Raydale and Cragdale. It is said that a village lies drowned beneath its surface and that it was a deliberate action by an unknown force because none of the villagers would give shelter or food to a stranger who sought their aid. The identity of that stranger has never been made known.

But it is another Yorkshire lake which is said to be magical, and that is Lake Gormire below Sutton Bank. It lies between Helmsley and Thirsk, and when he was Manager of N Y Estates, Turner would sometimes take a lunch break near Gormire. He would scramble down the steep incline to the shores of this serene lake, there to ponder upon its visible mystery.

'You see, Seth,' he said one night in the Woolpack, 'Gormire has no streams or rivers pouring water into it, and no outlet either. So where does the water come from, eh? And where does it go, Seth?'

'If I knew that, Mr Turner, I shouldn't be keeping fish for you, now would I?'

'And are there fish in Lake Gormire, Seth?'

'That's summat an expert like you should know, Mr Turner!'

'Yes, of course,' smiled Turner, uneasily.

There are some impressive waterfalls in the Yorkshire Dales and Moors. Pictured here is Hardraw Force in Wensleydale which pours over Hardraw Scar or Scaur, a cliff some thirty metres high. The people standing below give some idea of its scale, and in winter the roar of the water can be heard many miles away. It is located near the road which leads from Hawes over the Buttertubs Pass into Swaledale.

7

Kathy in town

IN those happy months before Jackie Merrick had died in such tragic circumstances, his pretty young wife, Kathy, had persuaded him to accompany her to the shops and supermarkets within convenient reach of Beckindale. At first, Jackie had pleaded there was too much work to do on the farm, that there were too many urgent jobs to complete and that he was far too busy to go shopping with her. Kathy had a sneaking suspicion that he regarded shopping as woman's work, but in time she had persuaded him to join her. And after a time he had quite enjoyed it.

But he had made some stipulations! He'd always insisted, for example, on having his lunch at lunchtime, whereas she would cheerfully forego that to maximise her time in the shops. She did not worry about eating while shopping, but if a break for lunch meant Jackie would accompany her, then she'd been prepared to compromise – especially when he had offered to pay!

Another of his conditions was that they did not spend *all* their time shopping.

She could hear him now. 'Look luv,' he'd said one day. 'The towns in Yorkshire have got lots of interesting places besides shops! Why don't we pretend we're tourists and look around?'

'Look around?' she'd asked.

'Yes, if we went to the supermarkets early and got the chores finished before lunch, we could spend time seeing the sights that tourists come to look at. I mean, here we are in the middle of all these historic and beautiful places, and we never see the interesting bits. We never go looking around York or Harrogate, do we? Or Halifax or Bradford? Folks come miles to see them, some even come from America, Japan and the continent, but we never bother. *We* should explore them!'

She had smiled and had welcomed his idea because it was true that many Yorkshire folk had never explored their own huge county with all its history and incomparable landscape. Besides, she could always go shopping – real shopping that is – with Dolly or Kate and spend time looking at shoes and dresses, trying on things and enjoying women's talk. And so, for a few months before Jackie's accident, they had done as he had wished. They had gone shopping early and they had visited the famous towns of Yorkshire to see the sights.

Kathy Merrick.

Now, tragically, she was alone, but she did find some solace in retracing those journeys, especially when she wanted to be on her own on a very personal pilgrimage.

With Jackie at her side, in their joint determination to visit every town in Yorkshire they did manage to visit Sheffield, an unusually handsome town in its impressive location among the hills. From Kathy's point of view it has the finest shopping centre in the country with over a mile of shops reaching from the Haymarket to The Moor via High Street and Fargate. There are seven markets, some of them indoors, although those like the traditional Moorfoot and the Setts are outdoors and selling everything from pots and pans to fruit and vegetables. Much of the shopping centre is pedestrianized, with shrubs, flowers and convenient seats – and a bandstand.

There are superb speciality shops and Kathy likes the multi-cultural atmosphere, the department stores, the antique and fashion shops, along with the cafes and tiny craft workshops which are so close to the town centre. For relaxation, she has discovered more than fifty parks and gardens and her one wish is to attend a concert or play at the Crucible Theatre which stages both classical and pop concerts. Jack Sugden had said she should go to the City Hall with its philharmonic concerts but she thought it might be a bit too highbrow for her! Besides, Jackie would never have gone there!

She did visit the City Museum in Weston Park and was astonished at the range of cutlery on display – then remembered that Sheffield is famous for its knives, forks and spoons whether in steel or silver! And she went to the industrial museum, known as Kelham Island, which came second in the Museum of the Year contest of 1982. There is a living museum at Graves Park, too, which contains water fowl and rare breeds of domestic animals.

But a short shopping visit left no time for true exploration of England's fourth largest city with its five river valleys, and Kathy is determined to revisit this fine town and to uncover more of its charms.

Bradford is also popular with the people at Beckindale. Like Sheffield this once had an industrial image which did not encourage visitors, but all that has changed and the city is now highly popular with visitors. It is high on Kathy's list for general shopping and it entails about an hour's drive into the city centre where parking is not a great problem. Up-to-date shops cater for most of Kathy's domestic needs.

Its old reputation of dust and dirt has gone and Bradford has been revealed as a fine town with handsome buildings and a long tradition of working closely with the sheep farmers of the dales. For centuries sheep have grazed the Yorkshire moors and fells to provide the nation's wool. Although many early farmers wove and treated their own wool, they could not cope with a larger, more professional market. For that, the wool had to be treated, woven and then marketed on a national and even international scale. There was a need to trade with almost every country in the world and Bradford fulfilled that role on their behalf. It became the world's central market for wool, and its products and its influence spread into the neighbouring towns where specialised products were made.

Huddersfield produced fancy worsted, the Colne Valley made tweeds while cheaper clothes came from Dewsbury, Batley and Morley. Bradford was proud of its dress cloths, and at Manningham Mills, the largest in the world,

Sheffield, famous for its steel and cutlery manufacture, is a handsome town impressively situated among steep hills in South Yorkshire. It boasts one of the finest shopping centres in the country.

Bradford is a fine town with some interesting buildings. Here is the Town Hall (right) with its tiered tower, and the distinctive shape of the Alhambra Theatre building (left). Note the old-style buses!

cotton and silk became a vital ingredient of the general industry – silk and velvet were made there. For Kathy Merrick, with her own small flock of sheep on Emmerdale's land, this was awe-inspiring, knowing that the care she lavished upon her animals was part of such a massive, world-wide enterprise.

While the fells and moors were ideal for breeding sheep, the lovely Pennine streams with their pure, lime-free water were perfect for washing, carding and combing the wool. Eventually, when steam power was harnessed to drive the machinery, Bradford became the country's biggest and most successful wool trading centre. It became a prosperous city, growing from a small town in a deep dale to a huge city spreading over the dale with some of its outlying areas rising to 1,000 feet above sea level. It has spawned hundreds of woollen mills, more than a hundred churches and chapels and miles of new streets full of houses which once accommodated those who worked in the woollen industry. Its fifteenth-century parish church of St Peter became a cathedral in 1920, and Bradford found itself pioneering social improvements such as free education for all, school meals for the poor children, the introduction of school doctors and social work in hospitals and clinics.

The town centre was gutted to make way for new developments; some buildings were reconstructed and modernised while others were cleaned and refurbished to highlight their ancient character and beauty. The post office would not look out of place in Italy, while the superb Town Hall can likewise be compared favourably to a Florentine building with its array of windows, parapets, gables and tiered tower. The Wool Exchange is adorned with a slender spire, rising to some 150 feet, and a statue of the patron saint of woolcombers, St Blaise. This is where wool merchants have met for gen-erations.

The town is also the country's main focus for educating students of the woollen industry, for its colleges boast the finest textile departments in the world. One spin-off has been the foundation of the Colour Museum. It shows the history of dyes and use of colour in textile printing as well as the value of colour in our everyday lives. In 1988 this was voted the Best Industrial Museum. There is, in addition, the Bradford Industrial Museum on Moorside Road with a nineteenth-century spinning mill, textile machinery and other aspects of educational interest. Jackie had liked its old vehicles – there were Jowett cars made in Bradford, Scott motor cycles and even a tram!

In exploring the city, Kathy liked to see the places where the famous used to live – a house in the town centre was the birthplace in 1863 of Frederick Delius, the composer, while the author J. B. Priestley was born in Manningham Road in 1894. Forster Square is named after William Edward Forster, a Bradford man whose work led to every child having the right to a free education, and in Darley Street there is a statue to honour Richard Oastler who created fury in the woollen industry by demanding shorter working hours for children. The creator of the model village of Saltaire, Sir Titus Salt, is honoured in Lister Park. He was once mayor of Bradford and his dream, Saltaire, was declared the healthiest working community in the world. It was built specifically as the home for working people, with all that they might want – except a pub!

Lister Park, in which his statue stands, is Bradford's pride and joy with its lawns, flowers, trees and boating lake – and a botanical garden claimed to be the largest outside London. Here is the Art Gallery and Museum which is inside Cartwright Hall. Built in 1904, this is in Baroque style and Jackie liked it because it has a permanent collection of twentieth-century art.

Bolling Hall, in Bolling Park, also houses a superb collection of social and local history; the Manor of Bolling dates from the Domesday Book and the oldest part of the existing building is probably 600 years old. When Jackie saw the Tudor kitchen, its larder with milk churns and a flail for threshing corn, he said it was probably how Emmerdale's kitchen looked when Grandad Pearson was a lad!

But Kathy loves the National Museum of Photography, Film and Television; among its attractions is the Imax screen, the largest in the United Kingdom which is so awesome that it makes you feel as if you are part of the action.

She remembers Jackie saying one day, 'I'm off to shoot the rapids with the Imax.'

To which Kathy had retorted, 'Then I'm going to look at some dresses!'

And now, as she returns to Bradford from time to time, she wishes she had shot the rapids with Jackie. But it isn't the sort of thing to do alone!

In retracing her haunts, she visited Halifax on its windswept Pennine site and toured the astonishing Piece Hall which was built in 1779. It encloses an open space of some 10,000 square yards in which a fruit and vegetable market has been held since 1871, but the Hall itself comprises a square of linked buildings, 311 rooms in all, which are two or three storeys high with a colonnade in front. It was here that the cloth merchants displayed their samples for sale and there is now a range of some fifty shops, plus an art gallery and museum.

Kathy can spend hours pottering around the Piece Hall but Halifax town is equally interesting and is probably the world's leading carpet manufacturing centre. Kathy did manage to buy a small off-cut for her cottage in Demdyke Row and she was delighted to find it was a replica of a tapestry in Bankfield, home of the art gallery and museum. There are looms and shuttles here, spinning wheels and the marvellous Crossley mosaics, which are tapestries made by machine. And there are reproductions of famous pictures such as works by Landseer, Raphael and other great artists.

She and Jackie had visited Ilkley, too, famous as the Heather Spa town because of its close proximity to the moors and its health-giving waters. It is also the home of the Yorkshire anthem, 'Ilkley Moor Bah't 'At,' and upon that moor there are the mysterious Cup and Ring carvings on stones, and an equally bizarre swastika drawn with curved lines. The latter is not from the

Halifax, set high in its Pennine location, is one of the world's première carpet manufacturing centres. The town centre contains some delightful old houses and inns which complement the sturdy parish church of St John the Baptist.

Nazis of the Second World War, for it was 1,000 years old when the Romans came to these moors. High on the moors, too, are the Cow and Calf Rocks, some caves in a dale known as Rocky Valley and a tarn which was once used for skating in winter. It was upon these hills, known as Rumbolds Moor, that springs of pure mineral water were found.

They gave birth to Ilkley as a fashionable spa. The town itself is charming. Solidly built of dark stone, it has wide streets, plentiful shops of quality, hotels, imposing public buildings, and all enhanced by hosts of trees and flowers. The church dates from the fifteenth century and contains some curious stones, one of which is believed to be Roman and to depict Hercules slaughtering a serpent. Another is thought to show a man holding a sacrificial container of wine, while three crosses in the grounds may each be over 1,000 years old.

But for Kathy, her favourite walk is from the town centre out to the Panorama Rocks. There she can sit with her memories while admiring the view across the dale far below, a dale beyond which lie the hills of Beckindale and home.

The Cow and Calf Rocks on Ilkley Moor in winter.

Harrogate is one of the most 'floral' of towns in Yorkshire, its streets and parks being a riot of colour.

Another town which fascinates Kathy is Harrogate; elegant and stylish, it is a romantic place full of flowers and classical shops. The Valley Gardens, home of the famous Spring Flower Show, are noted for their beauty, while the incredible Stray, a piece of common land extending to more than 200 acres in the heart of the town, is a riot of colour, especially in spring when thousands of crocuses bloom. It is like a mammoth lawn, neatly cut and trimmed but crossed by paths and roads and surrounded by fine houses and imposing hotels.

Harrogate has the claim of being 60 miles from both the east and west coasts of England, and 200 miles from both London and Edinburgh. Famed as a spa town since the time of Elizabeth I, Harrogate's initial inaccessibility did not encourage its popularity and it was the development of the railways in the last century that presented the town as the place that everyone of quality simply had to visit.

Fine hotels were built, along with shops, public buildings, a concert hall and other places of resort, all to cater for those who came to take the waters. The famous waters came from over eighty springs about the town, many of which were in Bogs Field. Bogs Field is now part of the Valley Gardens and it was here that thirty-six springs were found within an area of only one acre. No two were alike in chemical composition and it is believed this is unique throughout the world. This alone makes the Valley Gardens of immense interest, but the health-giving powers of these sulphur and iron waters led to Harrogate's international renown. In 1897 the Royal Baths Assembly rooms were built to cater for those who wished to either drink the water or bathe in it. The oldest spring, Kathy learned, was one found at Tewit Well just off the Leeds Road on the edge of the Stray where a plaque records that it was discovered by William Slingsby in 1571. It is now covered by a temple designed by Thomas Chippendale.

Most of the water from these various springs smelt awful, so much so that when the writer and traveller Celia Fiennes came, her horse would not go near it! But she drank a quart on two successive days, and it did not deter the very best of society who felt it was beneficial. During one day in 1911 no less than three Queens were in Harrogate at the same time, all to experience the waters. They were Queen Alexandria, the Empress Marie of Russia and Queen Amelie of Portugal. Poets such as Wordsworth, Southey and Byron came, too, as did Charles Dickens and others from the society of the period.

Another spa building was the Royal Pump Room, built in 1842, which covered the most popular of the mineral springs, the Sulphur Well near Royal Parade. Now a museum, it records the history of Harrogate from prehistoric times, and the original well is now in the cellar.

But modern visitors come not to drink the waters but to see the town and visit the surrounding countryside, although some come to work and attend conferences. Harrogate hosts an average of more than one conference per day throughout the year, many of them in the town's hotels, but there is a superb custom-built Conference Centre close to the six halls of the Exhibition Centre. The £31 million Conference Centre opened in 1982 and, during one trip, Jackie insisted that Kathy walk through the town to see this stunning structure. In fact, he bought her a cup of tea there.

But while Kathy loves Harrogate and nearby Knaresborough with its castle, gorge and Dropping Well which turns soft toys and clothes into stone, it is

One of the more modern buildings in Harrogate is the Conference Centre, opened in 1982 at a cost of £31 million.

York which is her favourite city for both shopping and sightseeing. She and Jackie often enjoyed walking on top of the city walls that encircle the old town. Away from the traffic, this allowed them to view the ancient streets from a superb vantage point. The complete walk is about two and a half miles, albeit with several breaks.

Kathy finds it astonishing that the present walls were the fourth to be constructed. The first were of earth and built by Hadrian, followed by stone walls constructed by the Roman emperor Severus. He can be called the Father of the City Walls, for his were followed by an earth and timber enclosure which the Norman invaders constructed. The final walls were built of huge blocks of stone with battlements and protective barriers to safeguard the city. They were built in medieval times and it was these very walls that Jackie had loved so much. The gates which led into the city are called Bars, and in some the ancient portcullis remains while Walmgate Bar still keeps its battlemented barbican. And on two stone pillars inside that gate, there is a tiny house which dates to the time of Elizabeth I.

So important was York in Roman times that it was known as 'The Other Rome', and called Eboracum; it was the headquarters of the British province of the Roman empire – even today, Roman relics continue to be unearthed during building operations, and years ago Roman graves were found when York Railway Station was built. The city is rich with scores of reminders of ancient Rome. One of them, which was buried for centuries, is a Roman tower which can be seen in the Museum Gardens; the tower is called the Multangular Tower.

The Museum Gardens, some ten acres in extent, contain the ruins of a medieval hospital, the ruins of St Mary's abbey, the Multangular Tower, the

A walk along the walls of York will reveal splendid views of the city with its ancient streets and famous buildings.

York Minster towers above the buildings which surround it.

Yorkshire Museum with its own displays of Roman relics, and some beautiful walks beside the River Ouse.

When the Vikings raided York, they cruised along the Ouse in their distinctive longboats and renamed it Yorvik. It was the Viking's capital of Northern England and second only to London in size and importance. Today their impact is preserved in the Yorvik Centre which stands upon the site of a former Viking settlement in Coppergate, and their lively February celebration of Jolablot has been revived. Jolablot heralded spring and honoured those who survived the winter; it is now enjoyed by citizens and visitors alike each February, even down to the ceremonial burning of a longboat. And deep within the Viking Centre is a reconstructed village through which visitors are transported on remote-controlled 'time cars'. These carry visitors through the streets of the village, complete with street sights, sounds and chatter, even accompanied by the smells of the bygone community.

The Normans came and built two castles here; there was their superb abbey of St Mary but Henry VIII demolished it during his Reformation and used the stones to build King's Manor.

A walk around the walls will reveal all these ancient influences, for the city centre streets remain narrow and winding with the houses so close in the Shambles that it is claimed people on opposite sides of the street can reach out of their bedroom windows and shake hands across the thoroughfare. There is a lovely story of a visitor to York in the days of horse-drawn coaches; he complained that there was no room for carriages to pass one another, where-upon a local man exclaimed, 'There's plenty of room, there's over an inch to spare!'

Those streets remain, and they are unsurpassed in their medieval quaintness and charm. There is Stonegate built over a Roman road with its fifteenth-century Mulberry Hall midway along, the Shambles which dates to the time of William the Conqueror and which was once full of butchers' shops, Coney Street named not after conies (rabbits) but after Kunung which means king, Spurriergate where spurs were made, Goodramgate named in honour of the Viking Guthrum, and Whipma-whopma-Gate where, it is said, criminals were whipped! Petergate, also upon the site of a former Roman road, the Via Principalis, is where Guy Fawkes was born and this opens to offer a unique view of the front of York Minster, the largest church of its kind in Europe. There is a story that when a South African soldier came to York and saw the splendour of the Minster he stood to attention and saluted it!

The west front is said to be one of the wonders of the world, and the church contains the largest area of stained glass in England, and probably in the world. The Minster's beginnings can be traced back more than 1,300 years when it was a little wooden church. Today it is a superb example of ecclesiastical architecture. Magnificent upon its historic site, it took 250 years to construct, and Kathy finds it entrancing every time she calls. Today there is little evidence of the damage caused by the terrible fire of 1984 when this superb Gothic church was threatened with total destruction.

But now, since Jackie's death, Kathy can often be seen admiring the medieval stained glass, especially the Five Sisters Window set in lead which came from Rievaulx Abbey. Or she might be spotted popping down to the Undercroft to see its ancient treasures, including the fascinating Horn of Ulph given by a relative of King Canute, or sometimes she will be noticed just sitting in one of the pews alone with her thoughts. On occasions, she is joined by Annie Sugden, two women of differing generations linked by a common grief. Now that traffic has been banned from the roads close to the Minster, there is total peace and tranquillity and each finds it a refuge in their busy lives.

For young and old, York's medieval streets are rich with charm, replete with history and yet filled with interesting shops, inns and restaurants to cater for all.

There are further gems like the Treasurer's House, the Assembly Rooms, the 500-year-old Guildhall, the Merchant Taylors' Hall, the Merchant Adventurers' Hall, the old Assize Courts and the Mansion House in which York's Lord Mayor resides during his term of office. The office of Lord Mayor in York was established by Richard the Second and the Mansion House is the only city hall in England which is purely the private home of the Lord Mayor and his Lady during their term of office. It is rich with tradition, with the official dinners still being held by candlelight.

Within a short distance of the city centre are York's City Art Gallery and its famous museums, such as the Castle Museum in the Eye of York, which is England's most popular historical museum of everyday life. It boasts some reproductions of Victorian street scenes, shop-fronts and period house rooms. There is the York Story Museum in the former church of St Mary in Castlegate; York Dungeon with its wax tableaux of Norse myths and medieval punishments and the Bar Convent Museum with its own special history of York and district, and regular displays of arts and crafts.

Before Jackie died, the Yorkshire Museum of Farming at Murton was of special interest to him due to its wide-ranging display of farming history, and he once took his great-grandad Sam Pearson to the National Railway Museum where they saw steam trains and railway memorabilia that caused Sam Pearson to chatter for months afterwards.

Another of York's collections is its ancient churches. Before the Reformation there were forty-one and this dwindled to around twenty-one earlier this century. Some date from the fourteenth and fifteenth centuries, and many are now used as community or arts centres – St Michael's near Ouse Bridge offers tasty lunches to all-comers. And now, on the rural outskirts, for people who love shopping, there are more shops, supermarkets and modern entertainments.

For all its ancient history, York is far from being a museum itself; it is alive and flourishing and it is a venue of which Kathy never tires.

8

Rachel in Brontë Country

JACK Sugden commented on Rachel's gloomy face as she walked from the school bus. 'So why such a misery?' he asked.

'We've got our subjects for "A" levels,' she told him. 'English Lit. Some of the modern books are fine, but we've also been given a copy of *Jane Eyre* to study. Why do they pick such old fashioned books? It'll be right boring, Jack.'

'Boring? It's anything but boring! Look, before you get into that book, why not find out all you can about Charlotte Brontë, the girl who wrote it? Do that first then you'll appreciate her work; you'll feel you know her.'

'Know her? How can I? She's been dead nearly 140 years!'

'I know, but you can get to know her. Look, she had a miserable life, a tragic life really. She lived in a remote place on the Yorkshire moors, a spot that's more isolated than Beckindale, so her knowledge and her books are remarkable. Look, Rachel, you're practising for your driving test, right? So if you promise to visit the Parsonage at Haworth and the other places associated with Charlotte, I'll let you use my car. I can teach you as you drive around Brontë country to get acquainted with the enigmatic Charlotte.'

'You mean there's places round here that she went to?'

'Lots of them,' he smiled. 'She might even have been to Beckindale! And she used those places in her books. So once you've seen her haunts, you should be able to recognise them in the book. That'll make it more interesting.'

She smiled her appreciation. 'Thanks, Jack,' she said. 'I'll do that, it sounds great.'

'Right, before you begin, have a look through the bookshelves in the parlour. My grandad collected a lot of books about Yorkshire. You'll find a lot of references to the Brontës. Check those before you go off to Haworth, find out as much as you can before you visit her old home, then you'll feel you know her at least a little.'

'You think she's not boring then?'

'Not if you like a story of passion, love and romance set in the wilds! You'll grow to love and admire Charlotte too. She was quite a lady – just you see.'

'Thanks, Jack,' she said. 'It sounds interesting already – more interesting than our teacher made it sound. Now, I'll put the kettle on.'

Rachel Hughes.

'That's a good start to anything,' beamed Jack as he followed her into the farm house. After a cup of tea, Rachel Hughes wasted no time starting her project. From grandad Pearson's small library she discovered that Charlotte Brontë was born at Thornton, which is now a suburb of Bradford. The date was Sunday, 21 April 1816.

The house, No. 74 Market Street, is still there. It has a commemorative plaque for it was here that the four famous Brontë children were born: Charlotte, Branwell, Emily and Anne. Their father, Patrick Brontë, was an Irishman and Rachel was delighted to discover he had been born on St Patrick's Day 1777 at a place called Emdale. That name was so like Emmerdale and it encouraged her to delve further.

But Emdale was not in Yorkshire. It was in County Down in Ireland and the young Patrick Brontë, then known as Brunty, had come to England to attend Cambridge University. After graduating in 1806, he met Maria Branwell, a well-educated but rather sickly girl from Cornwall. He became a curate at Hartshead high on the Pennines above the River Calder and they were married at Guiseley in December 1812. Two children, Maria and Elizabeth, were born at Hartshead before Mr Brontë moved to Thornton, but when he became perpetual curate at Haworth near Keighley, the family moved into the cold and awesome Parsonage on the edge of the moors.

Built of Yorkshire sandstone, it faces east towards the church and is separated from it by rows of tombstones. They provide a grim reminder of the days when the average age of a Haworth resident was only twenty-seven years. Today the cawing of the rooks in the branches above the graves adds a strange atmosphere to this solemn place.

When the family arrived at Haworth on 20 April 1820, the day before Charlotte's fourth birthday, the weary Mrs Brontë had only a further seventeen months to live. She died of cancer in September 1821 aged thirty-eight, leaving six tiny children. Mr Brontë sought the help of his wife's sister, Elizabeth, but she never understood the children and their father was always busy. Thus they found themselves spending most of their time in their rooms, alone. They did, however, own pets – Emily had a dog called Keeper, Anne had one called Floss, and Charlotte had a pair of pet geese called Adelaide and Victoria. They were not allowed playmates from the village and found refuge in stories they created about a fictitious world. They called them 'plays' and wrote them in tiny handwriting in miniature books. The writing was so tiny that a magnifying glass was needed to read them. They can still be seen in the Parsonage.

The children's knowledge was considerable, however, because Mr Brontë encouraged them to read newspapers and magazines, and to borrow books from the circulating library at Keighley. He had books, too, especially poetry by masters such as Wordsworth and Byron. When they went out, they found happiness and excitement in long walks across the desolate moors. Those walks

Hartshead Church. The Revd. Patrick Brontë was a curate at Hartshead on the Pennines when he married Maria Branwell. Their first two children, Maria and Elizabeth, were born at Hartshead.

can still be followed, and one of Charlotte's favourites was to a waterfall which she thought was magnificent, but which is really a rather small one, and there is an old chair-shaped rock and a stone clapper bridge which are a short walk from the Parsonage.

Rachel made up her mind to visit those places and, in the days that followed, she discovered many short references in Grandad Pearson's books. From those, she realised that life at the Parsonage must have been very strange and lonely. Even so, when little Maria and Elizabeth, aged ten and nine, were sent away on 1 July 1824 to a school for clergymen's daughters, they were desperately unhappy. The school was Cowan Bridge and on 10 August Charlotte, aged 8, also became a boarder there, with Emily following in November. Cowan Bridge was a hamlet between Leeds and Kendal on the River Leck. But the girls' health was harmed by the terrible conditions and they were taken home. Maria and Elizabeth died within a few months; Maria on 14 February 1825 at Haworth and Elizabeth on 6 May. They died of tuberculosis, then known as consumption. These poor children were buried beside their mother. Charlotte and Emily were withdrawn from the school and were taught at home by their father, along with Branwell and Anne. But it became necessary for the elder girls to go away for further education.

Worried and unhappy, Charlotte and Emily travelled by cart to Miss Wooler's School for Clergymen's Daughters at Roehead, twenty miles away on Mirfield Moor near Dewsbury. They started school on 19 January 1831. Charlotte was then fourteen and approaching fifteen. Their Aunt Elizabeth was prim, precise and old fashioned and had dressed the girls in curious out-

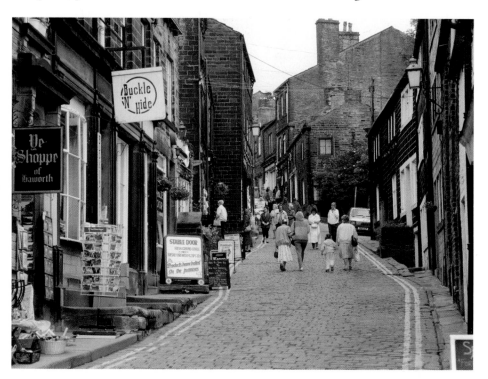

The village high street at Haworth down which Charlotte and members of the Brontë family would walk countless times.

One of Charlotte's favourite walks across the moors, often with her sisters and brother, was to a waterfall, a chair-shaped rock and a stone clapper-bridge. These are a short distance from the Parsonage at Haworth. The rock is known as The Brontë Chair, while the old stone bridge was damaged by floods in the spring of 1990. It was repaired with the assistance of a military helicopter which airlifted the five $1\frac{1}{2}$-ton stone slabs into position.

of-date clothes. She had made their hair frizzy, too, so when Charlotte arrived at school she was a strange sight and an object of fun to the other girls. One of her schoolmates, Mary Taylor, described her like this:

'I first saw her coming out of a covered cart, in very old-fashioned clothes and looking very cold and miserable. When she appeared in the schoolroom, her dress was changed but just as old. She looked a little old woman, so short-sighted that she always appeared to be seeking something and moving her head from side-to-side to catch sight of it. She was very shy and nervous and spoke with a strong Irish accent. When a book was given her, she dropped her head over it till her nose nearly touched it, and when she was told to hold her head up, up went the book after it, still close to her nose . . .'

Rachel Hughes learned that Charlotte was very conscious of her Irish accent, her short-sightedness, her old-fashioned hair style and, above all, her very plain appearance. She was desperately shy and nervous and was a very tiny,

The Parsonage at Haworth. Charlotte arrived here on 20 April 1820, the day before her fourth birthday, and was to spend much of her working life within its sombre walls. It is now a popular museum of Brontë exhibits.

frail child who was immediately marked as 'different'. Charlotte described herself as being stunted in growth but what dismayed her more at school was that she was considered rather stupid and placed in the lowest class. At Roehead she was very unhappy at first, especially as she could not enter the imaginary world she had created at Haworth. She could not produce the little plays, and said so in her diary, 'Far from home, I cannot write of them,' she recorded.

Emily was also unhappy at school and came home, then Charlotte left when she was sixteen. But while at Roehead she did make two sincere friends who remained loyal to her throughout her short, tormented life. They were Ellen Nussey and Mary Taylor, the girl who recorded her unhappy arrival. But Charlotte must also have impressed Miss Wooler because at the age of nineteen she was invited to become a teacher at Roehead. Probably out of a sense of duty, she accepted. But she soon found she could not cope with a life of working for others, and later neither could Emily or Anne who became governesses with private families. Eventually the sisters went home to start their own school – the Parsonage was large enough, they could then spend time walking the moors and, besides, they now had to earn money to help their father. To gain the experience necessary to become teachers, Charlotte and Emily went to a school in Brussels in 1842 to study languages. This was to change Charlotte's life and form the basis of her timeless novels because at the Pensionnat she fell hopelessly in love.

She was now twenty-five and the object of her affections was the Principal, Monsieur Constantin Romain Heger, who, at thirty-three, was several years older than Charlotte. He was also happily married to a beautiful wife with auburn hair and blue eyes. Charlotte was fascinated by Heger – he had a strong chin and dark eyes, and was swarthily handsome, virile, very capable, confident and talented, as well as being kindly, wise, good and religious with a magnetic personality. He was a Roman Catholic, too, and had a family of small children. But he did not return her affections and was probably embarrassed by her juvenile attentions. At this revelation, Rachel found herself blushing, for she had also fallen in love with a married man, Pete Whitely . . .

But after only one year, Charlotte and Emily had to leave Brussels to attend to family matters after Aunt Elizabeth died. M. Heger said he was sorry to lose Charlotte, whom he regarded as a very promising student, and the girls returned to Haworth, sorrowing at yet another death in the family. But this was not the end of Charlotte's time in Brussels.

Charlotte loved Birstall and always enjoyed visiting the town. It was the home of her friend Ellen Nussey and it features in her books. Oakwell Hall became 'Fieldhead' in Shirley *and Ryddings may be 'Thornfield Hall' in* Jane Eyre.

Lothersdale. Near the church is a house called Stonegappe which is 'Gateshead' in Jane Eyre. *In 1839 Charlotte worked here as a governess and hated it.*

She returned in January 1843, intending to stay a further year to study teaching at the Pensionnat and was welcomed by the Hegers. She found herself increasingly drawn to the handsome Constantin and, although he did remain aloof from any love affair, he did show affection and friendship. In her childish way she might have misinterpreted his actions, but Madame Heger did become concerned about their relationship.

Soon Charlotte abandoned the course, unhappy about her unrequited love but determined to open her own school. Full of enthusiasm, she and Emily produced a circular (which can still be seen), drew up their curriculum, prepared the rooms for the incoming young ladies and waited. But no one came.

Then Charlotte, having turned to writing poetry, chanced in the autumn of 1845 to peep into Emily's writing desk. There she found some poems. Emily accused Charlotte of snooping, but then Anne produced some of hers and so did Charlotte ... excited, they decided to print a book of their work and sell it. They used the peudonyms of Acton, Currer and Ellis Bell, the first names beginning with their own initials. The printing cost £31, and when it was published they settled down to await customers. None came. Only two copies of the book were sold. Still determined to succeed, the three girls turned their attention to what they called prose tales. Rachel knew this was their word for novels. Emily, now very sick and growing weaker, wrote *Wuthering Heights*; Anne wrote *Agnes Grey* and Charlotte wrote *The Professor*.

All were rejected. It was almost too much for the girls. Tired, sick, weak, dejected and heartbroken, their will was almost crushed. Their walks to the chair rock and to the waterfall became fewer, their father was sick while their brother Branwell was drunk, drugged and insufferable, and it was clear he had tuberculosis. Then one Sunday he struggled out of bed, stood up and died on his feet. He was just thirty-one.

In the meantime, the girls' three novels were being re-submitted to publishers, and all were turned down. Then a publisher said he would accept *Wuthering Heights* and *Agnes Grey*, but only if the authors would contribute towards publication. *The Professor* continued to receive rejections. But Charlotte was to prove strong and indefatigable.

She arranged to take her father to Manchester for an eye operation, and on the morning she departed, *The Professor* was rejected yet again, but the publisher said he wished to see more of the author's work. That night, Charlotte sat down to begin *Jane Eyre*. In August 1847 she sent off the completed manuscript. It was written under the pseudonym Currer Bell. The publisher was so thrilled with the book that he sent it immediately to the printer and it was published in October the same year – it was an instant and resounding success. And it continues to sell today.

Quite suddenly, Charlotte Brontë, the dull, plain and shy little teacher from Yorkshire, was fêted by the literati of London as a major English novelist. Although still very uneasy with strangers, she met Thackeray (who gave a dinner in her honour), Dickens, Matthew Arnold and Mrs Gaskell, who was to become her biographer. The publisher, when re-examining the other novels, thought they were all by the same writer. He was astonished when three girls went to London to reveal their true identities.

But Emily and Anne never lived to enjoy their own success. Emily was thirty when she died in December 1848. The settee on which she was lying when she died is still in the parlour of the Parsonage. And a few months later Anne died while visiting Scarborough; she is buried in St Mary's Churchyard there, the only Brontë not buried at Haworth. Charlotte was with her when she died.

Charlotte was now alone with her elderly father and continued to live at Haworth. There she wrote her next novel, *Shirley*, based on Emily's life and set in Calderdale.

Keighley Railway Station is still used by steam trains of the Keighley and Worth Valley Steam Railway. Charlotte walked to the station from Haworth in a thunderstorm to catch a train to London to reveal her identity to her publisher.

It was nearly eleven o'clock when Rachel ended that session among Grandad's books, and when Jack came into see how she was progressing she was alight with enthusiasm.

'What you must do next,' his dark eyes were full of joy at her dedication, 'is to find out more about Charlotte's sad love affairs and then you'll see how she really suffered – she used them, and some of the local countryside, in her novels.'

'I feel really sorry for her – for them all,' Rachel said.

'So you know Charlotte a bit better, eh?'

'Poor woman, yes. So what about her love life, Jack?'

'Well, it's late, and it's time you were in bed, but I'll whet your appetite. You can see why Charlotte did not attract many men – she was too plain, too shy and, besides, she did not have the opportunity to meet them. For a while she taught at Sunday school, the one near the Parsonage but I don't think she experienced romance. It wasn't until she went to Brussels that she fell in love. She always wanted to fall in love, but as early as twelve said she was destined to be an old maid. She told Ellen Nussey, her school friend, that if she ever did marry, her husband must inspire an attachment so intense that she would willingly die for him! She said that if she ever married, it must be in the light of adoration.'

'She must have had a teenage crush though?' asked Rachel.

'Mebbe later than teenage!' countered Jack. 'You know about her ill-fated romance in Brussels?'

Jack paused. He knew Rachel could appreciate the hurt that must have affected Charlotte.

'Heger never returned her love, though,' Jack went on. 'I think he regarded it as an embarrassing crush; his wife, however, kept an eye on the pair of them, just in case!'

'Poor Charlotte . . . how awful. Didn't she ever find love?'

'Well, after her brother's and sisters' deaths, she grew very, very lonely; she lived in intense and painful solitude, broken only by her trips to London to

Charlotte Brontë was born at No. 74 Market Street, Thornton, near Bradford, on Sunday 21 April 1816. Her brother Branwell and two younger sisters, Emily and Jane, were also born here.

mingle with writers and publishers and I'm sure that did give her pleasure. Then she became very friendly with her publisher, George Smith.'

'She didn't become Mrs Smith, did she?' laughed Rachel.

'No, there was no romance, but they were friends. He once took her to see the famous French actress called Rachel – that was her stage name. Charlotte's friend, Ellen Nussey, thought it might lead to a love affair, but Smith had no such inclinations. One of his staff, however, did love Charlotte; he was called James Taylor. He went to Haworth and proposed, but she did not return his affections. She thought he was odd! She had another admirer in Ellen Nussey's brother, himself a clergyman, but that came to nothing. In fact, he proposed to her in February 1839; he was Henry Nussey who was curate to the Revd. Charles Lutwidge at Burton Agnes in the East Riding.

'He was the uncle of Charles Lutwidge Dodgson, better known as Lewis Carroll, the author of *Alice in Wonderland*. But it was another curate who finally won her heart. He was called Arthur Nicholls.'

'Really? Was he tall, dark and handsome?' smiled Rachel.

'Well,' said Jack. 'He was good-looking with a strong face, dark hair and whiskers and bright eyes. He worked hard but he was bigoted in his religious outlook – Charlotte said he lacked fine talents and tastes. But he fell in love with her, and one day he came into her study, trembling all over, and he asked her to marry him. Charlotte said she must ask her father, but when he did the old vicar threw out poor Arthur and recruited a new curate. That one was terrible, so he recalled Arthur. And he said Charlotte could marry Arthur provided they lived at the Parsonage to look after him.'

'Oh, how lovely!' breathed Rachel.

'The wedding day was on 29 June 1854, and Charlotte wore a white muslin dress, a white lace mantle and a bonnet trimmed with green leaves.'

'Green's unlucky at a wedding!' breathed Rachel.

'The villagers said she looked like a little snowdrop but her father refused to attend the wedding, he would not even give her away. That was done by her old teacher and friend, Miss Margaret Wooler from Roehead. They honeymooned in Ireland, where Charlotte fell off a horse, and after they came back Charlotte soon found herself pregnant.

'That was in the autumn of 1854. The following spring, Arthur walked her to her favourite waterfall when the snow was melting and she caught a cold. She died that March, only nine months after being married. She had been so happy with Arthur and her last words were, "We have been so happy." Arthur remained at the Parsonage to look after old Mr Brontë who outlived his entire family. He died in 1861, aged 84, having been cared for by Arthur. And Charlotte's first book, *The Professor*, was published after her death.'

'What a sad, sad story,' whispered Rachel.

'Right, off to bed with you,' said Jack. 'I'll write out a list of places around here for you to visit, they're all associated with Charlotte. Then you can visit the Parsonage.'

'Thanks,' she said.

Jack was as good as his word. He listed these places:

Haworth village near Keighley

The Parsonage – with its original scripts and exhibits. See the fir trees planted by Charlotte and Arthur.

The church – with its Brontë vault.

The churchyard – with its graves of Tabitha and Martha, the faithful servants of the Brontës.

The Sunday school – between the church and Parsonage where Charlotte taught.

The Black Bull Inn – where Branwell entertained his pals.

Brontë Falls, Chair and Bridge – favourite walks of all the Brontë children. You can walk here from Haworth.

The village high street – imagine Charlotte walking down here.

Other places

Keighley and Worth Valley Railway – a five-mile track with steam trains running between Keighley and Oxenhope. 'The Railway Children' was filmed here. Charlotte used this line to travel to London to see her publishers, travelling from Keighley Station.

Keighley – Charlotte walked the four miles from Haworth to Keighley to buy her writing paper and reading books. She became very distressed if the shop was out of paper, and so, to please her, the shop keeper would walk ten miles to Halifax to obtain stocks for her. Charlotte walked to Keighley Railway Station in a thunderstorm to catch the train to London to reveal her identity to her publisher. She also accompanied Anne from here to Scarborough; Anne died four days later.

Thornton, Bradford – birthplace of Charlotte (21 April 1816), Branwell (26 June 1817), Emily (30 July 1818); and Anne (17 January 1820). They were born at No. 74 Market street, and were baptised in the parish church.

Hartshead – between Brighouse and Cleckheaton. The Revd. Patrick Brontë was vicar here when he married Maria Branwell. Their eldest children, Maria and Elizabeth, were born here. Charlotte called the village Nunneley in *Shirley*.

Kirkstall Abbey, Leeds – Patrick Brontë here proposed to Maria Branwell while she was on holiday from Cornwall. The abbey is not far from Yorkshire Television's studio in Leeds.

Kirklees Park near Huddersfield – the reputed burial place of Robin Hood and probably the 'Nunwood' in *Shirley*.

Birstall – an industrial town loved by Charlotte. It was the home of her friend Ellen Nussey and features in two of Charlotte's books. Oakwell Hall is 'Fieldhead' in *Shirley*. Another fine house, Ryddings, may be 'Thornfield Hall' in *Jane Eyre*. It was Ellen's home and Charlotte had happy times there. Her school mistress, Miss Margaret Wooler, is buried here. She survived to enjoy the success of her former pupil and great friend.

Bolton Priory – in the summer of 1833 Charlotte and Ellen Nussey hired a pony and gig and went on a day trip to Bolton Priory with Branwell, Emily and Anne. They left Haworth between 5 and 6 am, and met friends of Ellen's at Bolton Priory.

Gomersall – Charlotte came to see Red House and then wrote of it as 'Briarmains' in *Shirley*. It was the home of Hiram Yorke.

Mirfield – a market town on the River Calder. Roehead was the school to which Charlotte, Emily and Anne went as boarders, but they longed for their home on the moors. Charlotte returned here for a while as a teacher.

Wycoller near Colne – the now-ruined hall became the setting for 'Ferndean Manor' in *Jane Eyre*.

Lothersdale – near the church is a house called Stonegappe, the 'Gateshead' in *Jane Eyre*. In 1839 Charlotte worked as a governess for the Sidgwicks at Stonegappe and hated it. She went with the family to stay at Swarcliffe Hall in Nidderdale near Birstwith, not far from Harrogate.

When Charlotte saw Red House at Gomersall, she wrote of it as 'Briarmains' in Shirley, *when it was the home of Hiram Yorke.*

In Charlotte's time,
Bridlington was known as
Burlington. She came to the
town in September 1839,
aged twenty-three, and it was
her first visit to the seaside.
It was also her first ride on a
train. She was stunned by
the magnificent bay and asked
to be left alone to view it.

Cowan Bridge near Kirby Lonsdale – the then infamous School for Clergymen's Daughters at Cowan Bridge run by the Revd. W. Carus-Wilson. Four of the Brontë girls boarded here. Charlotte hated it and the oppression that was used here. Her hatred is shown in *Jane Eyre* when she features the school as 'Lowood' and noted that forty-five out of the eighty pupils were ill at one time. The food was foul, the accommodation primitive.

Bridlington – on the coast of East Yorkshire, it was once known as Burlington. Ellen Nussey and Charlotte came here for a holiday in September 1839. It was Charlotte's first visit to the seaside and her first ride on a railway train. She said the idea of seeing the sea and watching its changes by sunrise, sunset, moonlight and noonday filled and satisfied her mind. When she did see it, she was stunned by the magnificent bay and asked to be left alone to view it, her hands trembling and her eyes running with tears.

Scarborough – on the coast of North Yorkshire. Charlotte came here with Anne and was with her at her death. Anne is buried in St Mary's Churchyard, Scarborough.

Filey – on the coast of North Yorkshire near Bridlington. Charlotte stayed at Cliff House near Crescent Gardens in 1849 after Anne's death. She found the atmosphere quieter than Scarborough and liked long walks upon the deserted beach. She was amused that the choir singers in church all turned their backs upon the parson while singing.

Rawdon near Bradford – in March 1841 Charlotte came to work for the White family as a governess at Upperwood House. She did not like Mrs White and stayed only a year.

Norton Conyers near Ripon – this large country house was probably visited by Charlotte in 1839 when visiting Swarcliffe Hall with the Sidgwick family. Here, she learned of the legend of the mad woman who was kept in the attic and may have used the story in *Jane Eyre*.

Hathersage near Sheffield – in 1845 Charlotte holidayed with Ellen Nussey at Hathersage on the Yorkshire/Derbyshire border. Here she found the Eyre family memorials in the parish church and saw the family home at North Lees, so like Thornfield in *Jane Eyre*.

The Lake District – after staying at Gawthorpe Hall near Burnley, the home of Sir James and Lady Shuttleworth, Charlotte went to the Lake District in the summer of 1850. She stayed with the Shuttleworths at Briery Close on the shores of Windermere. Another guest was Mrs Elizabeth Gaskell who was later to write the biography of Charlotte Brontë.